BR
161-

D1108185

THE WOODSHED

A man on holiday in Wales receives late one night a message which seems to indicate that his father is dying. Next day, Harold Atha returns to a small house in the industrial West Riding. It is a journey both in place and in time.

Mr Heppenstall does not waste words. The close-woven fabric of his novel glitters with the scenes, characters and incidents of Atha's early years, some humorous, some grim, but all (though in essence common to most men) endued with a unique flavour of intellectual excitement. The atmosphere of Hinderholme, upon which Atha's memories are centred, and of a smaller town in the North Riding is magically conveyed.

In a review of *The Connecting Door*, to which the new novel is in part a sequel, Philip Toynbee wrote of Mr Heppenstall (in *The Observer*) as 'a writer who has given us so much that is beautiful, so much that is funny, and so much that is good'. Readers of *The Woodshed* will endorse that view. We may be allowed to add that Mr Heppenstall has also given us so much that is original.

RAYNER HEPPENSTALL

The Woodshed

BARRIE AND ROCKLIFF
LONDON

© RAYNER HEPPENSTALL 1962
FIRST PUBLISHED 1962 BY
BARRIE AND ROCKLIFF (BARRIE BOOKS LTD.)
2 CLEMENT'S INN, LONDON WC2
PRINTED IN GREAT BRITAIN BY
ROBERT CUNNINGHAM AND SONS LTD.
LONGBANK WORKS, ALVA

CONTENTS

THE WOODSHED

I

A YOUNG MAN WALKED BRISKLY PAST ABOUT TEN minutes before we started. He must have settled near the front of the train, and they can't have walked forward as far as that before turning back. They must have thought I was the only other passenger on the train. They got in with me.

That sort of gregariousness is not only beyond my understanding. I'd not even met it before, not even in the Army. In battle perhaps, or just before or just after, when you were all so apprehensive or so fagged out that there was some point in huddling together. You could understand some old lady, unaccustomed to travelling by train, worried about where she had to change.

Perhaps they assumed that *I* was from Birmingham and were homesick as a result of talking to none but Welsh people. Hardly. All this week, the beach has been full of Birmingham voices. They are hearty, uninhibited people, still young. If they use their eyes at all, they can hardly have found much promise in my pale, disagreeable face at the window. At any rate, in they got, six of them, two men in their early thirties (the big one perhaps under thirty), their very presentable wives and the two little girls.

I wish I could have made it plain that I did not dislike them. I shouldn't have liked the little girls to clamber over my knees, as they would certainly have done with the least sign of encouragement from me, but otherwise I found their physical presence agreeable. The men with their clean, open-necked, white shirts, the women in freshly ironed cotton frocks, one of the women really very handsome in a big, opulent way that reminded me of A'ntie Ada, all of them lobster-pink and smelling of sun and sea. No doubt in a few weeks from now they will smell of axle-grease, dust and week-end beer, but at that moment one felt in them all the joyousness of dry, salty, rested bodies copulating in strange beds, people seeing each other newly with sun-dazzled eyes.

At some other time, I might even have tolerated the children crawling over me as they crawled over the lean knees of their fathers, the fleshy thighs of their mothers. But I had my own preoccupations. Inwardly, I was in some distress.

A fortnight ago, I was still in the Rhineland. It would be *that* Thursday afternoon when I went for a last walk round the Orangerie. Then Arlette in Paris, then back to London on the Monday. Blod and the children were already down here. I got my third piece in at *The Examiner*, saw to one or two things at Matthew Latimer's and followed on, yes, that was Friday of last week. So I'd been at Gwaelod just five days when the sergeant called.

Five days and four hours. Five and one hour when the

message came through from Hinderholme. Exactly five, to the hour, when my sister went down to the police station at Ellen Brig. Getting from London to Gwaelod takes longer than it does from Paris to London. I arrived at seven o' clock. The 'bus stopped at the top of the hill, and I looked down on the dark-blue, damp slate roofs, tier below tier. You couldn't, on that bit of coast, so build two rows of houses parallel with the sea that the foundations of the one row didn't stand on a higher level than the roof tops of the other.

Nice in some ways. To that side of the harbour, all the front windows have an unbroken view over Cardigan Bay. At his front door, everybody can turn right and, in clear weather, see the white tops of Cader Idris and Snowdon glittering in the sun. On the other hand, the way out to your back garden lies upstairs, and heavy rain washes the soil away from the roots of your lettuces and deposits it, together with earthworms, wire-worms and centipedes, on top of the dustbins and under the kitchen door.

Gwladys Fainwright's cottage stands in a long row on the elevated sea-front, to that side, south of the harbour. In the roadway, the only traffic is tradesmen's vans and a municipal rubbish truck. Even now, pretty nearly at the height of the season, few people walk by. The street ends in a disused slate-quarry, beyond which you proceed at your peril.

In front of each cottage, a square of concrete affords either leg-room for three chairs in a row or bouncing-space for two balls. The front gardens lie across the narrow road, behind a low wall. Three good strides more, and you would be over the cliff. A deep cavern is said to lie beneath the houses themselves. If you stand in one of those gardens, get somebody to hold you by the hand and lean forward, you look down upon rocks over which swirls a sea discoloured with municipal rubbish dumped over the cliff's edge from the old quarry.

Some cottages have glass porches built over their front doors. Others have been pebble-dashed all over. The mats are shaken every morning. The steps and the curtains are spotless. In most of the windows stands a fern or an aspidistra. In other windows there are brass cages containing indignant parrots.

Even Gwladys Fainwright's cottage manages to look clean from the outside, no doubt because of the spray and the salt winds. The state of things inside was Kenneth Fainwright's fault. That is the trouble with psycho-analysts. If it ever came freely into Gwladys's head to do some cleaning, Kenneth would rejoice, not because a state of comparative order and comfort then seemed likely to ensue, but because Gwladys had found a new form of self-expression, which might be expected to keep her happy for a while and so lower the nervous tension all round. It would never occur to him that he could require any house in which he lived or stayed to be habitable.

There are two rooms downstairs, with a concrete-floored kitchen into which no daylight penetrates, a coal-cellar and the most indispensable of the usual offices. Upstairs, there are three small bedrooms, from one of which you pass directly into another if you succeed in raising a stiff iron catch. This catch, as it yields at last with a sound like the crack of a ringmaster's whip, is then either torn from your grasp by the wall-paper-puncturing, plaster-bespattering door, in which case you are lucky, or it drags you forward and down, your feet leaving you at the same moment as your fore-head and the lintel came together.

Still, I suppose awkwardnesses of that kind are a characteristic of cottages in general and could hardly, of themselves, give rise to protest. A paraffin stove, too, is one of those engines of doom which anyone bent on the simple life may encounter. Inches of dust, beneath which lie stacked empty but unwashed jam-jars, bottles and packets formerly containing breakfast-food, cannot, however, or so Blod felt, be regarded as a normal hazard. Neither can an exhibition of Gwladys Fain-wright's landscapes on every sooty wall. Nor is every-body who lives in the country or by the sea compelled to drink out of hand-made pottery, which, because the source of replacement lies eight hours away in London, cuts into the lips with chipped brown rims a quarter of an inch wide.

Poor Gwladys. It is, I am sure, a good thing that her pottery fetches a high price in Chelsea and Wigmore Street. As to her pictures, it is simply that, once we had closed the door on Gwaelod, I, at least, would rather have had done for the day with lobster-pots, seagulls, lighthouses, upturned boats and drying nets. Those high-pitched colours and disarticulated forms suddenly gain intensity under an artificial light.

The weather has not been good. For the first three days, a sea-fret drifted streakily inland. The air was then somewhat cleared by a gale, which kept a triangu-lar sleeve climbing the flag-pole on the jetty. The sky remained overcast, however, except first thing in the morning and towards sunset, when the mountains of North Wales briefly appeared. Yet we read in the papers that, inland, there was prolonged sunshine.

Over the week-end, the bulk of the visitors were still Welsh, as we learned tentatively on Saturday and with certainty on Sunday evening. For then took place a spontaneous movement to the pier-head and a singing borne magically across the bay, perhaps faintly echoed in the land beneath the waves, upon which a famous drunkard opened the sluice-gates and let in the sea.

Certainly, Welsh was the only language to be heard in the road outside Gwladys Fainwright's cottage. Next door, on the side towards the quarry, lives an idiot boy, allowed out only in the evening, when, with happy cries, he rushes up to any child still playing in the road (usually my Lewis or the nephew next door on the other side) and strikes it. Even he spoke Welsh, a remarkable achievement for an idiot boy. On the beach, however, on Monday morning, Birmingham, Liverpool, Manchester and even Cockney were to be heard in small but emphatic quantities.

There have begun to be holiday crowds. You might have expected Gwaelod to remain quiet, while the populace milled and sweated in Aberystwyth to the north. It has clearly got around that Gwaelod possesses a good beach for children. Thirty miles inland, between the coast and the infant Wye, lie the Birmingham Corporation reservoirs. If the people of Birmingham, stirring with summer restlessness, migrate due west, they are bound to end up somewhere along the shores of Cardigan Bay, where, lacking any pastime more familiar to them, they will occupy themselves in laming little girls with cricket-balls, pelting with pebbles the occasional basking seal and cracking with sticks the delicate pink glasswear of stranded cuttlefish.

The sergeant would be coming off duty. It was nearly midnight when he called. I had been trying to write at the front window, distracted by a school of porpoises, as a leaden daylight faded over the bay, closing us in. All day, a fog-signal had boomed. All evening, I had seemed to feel the presence of the Fainwrights themselves, Gwladys in a tea-cosy hat, her front teeth raised in a faint smile, hoping to complete with success the difficult operation of making tea, Kenneth, at fifty still a boy, anxiously watching the little psyche unfold, afraid to touch it.

The children were asleep. Old Flowerface and I lay side by side in two creaking and precarious camp-beds. I answered the knock.

'Mr Atha?' said the sergeant.

'Yes.'

In that case, the sergeant had a message for me. Did I know a Mrs Binns? I pondered. Ah, yes. Marjorie, my sister, had been Mrs Binns for a year and more.

The Hinderholme police had telephoned at eight o'clock, but there had been nobody at the station to send. I offered the sergeant gin, that being all we had. He was afraid he didn't touch it. He murmured sympathetically and went.

I rejoined Blod, cursing. I could do nothing at the moment, of course. Even if there had been a night train from Aberystwyth, there was no way of getting into Aberystwyth.

This morning, my sister's telegram followed. Blod went round to see Captain Lloyd, who runs a car for hire. He was already out on another job. I had to go to the bank. It was almost half past twelve by the time I got to Aberystwyth. The next train was after one o'clock. Cigarettes have been a trouble all week. Luckily, they had some on the station. I was smoking the second of these when the double trio from Birmingham joined me.

Once the train had started, with amiable smiles I stepped over their feet, pulled back the stiff door and walked along the corridor. That would seem normal. All the other compartments in that coach were, as I had supposed, empty. I decided which I would sit in and then went back.

I stepped over the four pairs of feet which reached the floor, smiling amiably, murmuring apologetically, lifted my suitcase off the rack, stepped over the feet again, keeping up both the murmurs and the smiles, and left the compartment.

As, with a last, rather despairing smile, as though I had been compelled to withdraw by forces beyond my control (the discovery, *e.g.*, that an important business contact was sitting in a first-class compartment along the corridor), I pushed the intendedly sliding door shut, the smaller, plainer of the two women said:

'He don't seem to like us.'

At least, I think she did. It is what I should have expected her to say.

THAT WAS BORTH. THIS IS YNYS-LAS. THE TIDE IS out. The wide estuary is all wet sand, with a narrow stream in its channel half way across. That is the Dyfi, which divides North from South Wales. Across the estuary lies Aberdovey. There is a song called 'The Bells of Aberdovey'. Blod sings it to the children, I suppose to teach them the Welsh numerals (teach me, too). It goes:

> *Un, dau, tri, pedwar, pump, chwech, saith,*
> *Meddai clychau Aberdyfi . . .*

The tune is without merit.

Now Glan Dyfi. The white raised letters on black, white-rimmed cast-iron glare in this disturbed sunlight, in at the window. A heron among the reeds, as we climb towards Machynlleth. Telegraph poles pass the window, not too fast but gathering speed. From right to left they rise to the vertical and fall away. *Un, dau, tri, pedwar, pump, chwech, saith, wyth, naw. . . .* A giant on stilts, hurrying to the sea, lifts one leg out of the ooze, then slaps it smartly down as he raises the other. Perhaps that unfortunate giant in the *Mabinogion* tale, not the one about Blodeuedd or Blodeuwedd, the original Flowerface, turned into an owl.

Turned into an owl for infidelity. Not old Flowerface, my Blod. I'd be the one turned into an owl. Idwal John, J.P., was never a baker. A grocer's boy when his mother first wept him up from the pit. No, a butcher's boy. Groceries later. Both her father and mine must have served flour with a scoop from square zinc bins. They never met. They won't meet now.

In a train, your consciousness streams like a cold.

Mr A. regrets. Mr A. is confined to his carriage with a streaming consciousness. If I had a secretary sitting opposite with shorthand notebook, or a dictaphone, I could just talk like this. They reckon about ten thousand words to the hour. In a journey of eight hours, you could finish a book. Change the names, and you'd have a stream-of-consciousness novel. A man travelling somewhere for a purpose. What had led up to it, hopes and fears, retrospect and apprehension mingling, things noted as the landscape slid by. At the end, some kind of pay-off. The fears were groundless, the person was not there or had changed his mind, some accident took place, the person or place no longer existed. Had just died perhaps.

I suppose he is dying. Neither message was clear, but nobody's thought of calling me home before. They wouldn't *expect* me. Not like Blod, who's always gone home at the least sign of trouble in her family. My sister's there. Now that she's Mrs Binns and lives in Lancashire, she wouldn't be there in mid-week if things were normal.

Possibly something else. I was told asthma was never a killing disease.

In which room? It could be any of the three. What used to be mine at the back had become Marjorie's by the time I was there during the war. I suppose things of hers will still be in it. I slept in the little front room, with a square hole in the wall over the bed-head to let light into the box-room. In that little front room is where A'ntie Beulah died while I was in Egypt, there being nobody at Bradford Road to look after her.

It will be the little front room. Between turns of

sitting up with him, my mother will sleep in the double bed in the big room. There will be drawn curtains in day-time, a candle at night.

Between the step-ladder, the trunk and the stacked suit-cases, beneath the shelves of jams and pickles, I used to imagine a boggart lived. On tip-toe, it could look down, from the square hole in the wall over the bed-head, on anyone sleeping in the little front room. As Marjorie or our mother dozed by candlelight, it would look down last night on my father's uneasily turning head.

I suppose that I could have detected the seeds of death in him last November. My sister married her Lancashire man in May, and it would have been in February that my father retired, being then sixty-five.

His colleagues at Molethorpe presented him with a bed-tray. The drapery managers from other co-operative societies, whom he had been accustomed to meet on Tuesday afternoons at the C.W.S. in Hinderholme, presented him with an umbrella whose engraved silver ring expressed their pleasure in twenty-five years' association with him. For the first few days and intermittently over a week or two, his breakfast was brought upstairs and served to him on the bed-tray, but this was a strain on my mother's ironclad leg, and he soon discontinued the habit.

There were still half a dozen Rhode Island Red hens, kept at the back in what had once, before we moved into that house, been an outdoor privy, solidly built in the local sandstone. That had then been the end of the garden. On the ground which extended it into the allotments, in a small greenhouse, electrically heated and thermostatically controlled, his vine still yielded in autumn numerous bunches of small grapes.

He collected on behalf of the Royal Infirmary, where, eight years before, my mother had lain so long and towards which he felt a sense of obligation. At the time of the municipal elections, he did some envelope-addressing at the Ellen Brig town hall, but what he got paid for that was deducted from his and my mother's combined old-age pension.

His weekly consumption of beer had never amounted to more than one pint or two, consumed in half-pints on Wednesday and Saturday evenings. He could no longer afford to go even so often to the Woolpack. My parents' total income was now their combined pension of two guineas a week, though luckily they owned the house and everything in it. My father also went short of cigarettes. Old-age pensioners are allowed a certain number of cigarettes at a reduced rate. My mother does not smoke. Her conscience wouldn't allow her to take her quota of cheaper cigarettes, or my father might have had twice as many.

It was to do with A'ntie Ada's piano that I went home in November. I'd always thought of the piano in the front room at home as mine. Neither of my parents played. Marjorie had left home. In London, I had room for a piano but not enough money to buy one. Erica Jo was forgetting her notes. I wondered if I could now have the piano. It had been promised to Marjorie as a wedding present. She would be having it moved in due course.

This was explained in a letter. My parents must have feared that I should feel aggrieved and have mentioned the matter outside, for they also said that A'ntie Ada had offered me what had once been Grandad Sykes's piano. A few pounds were to be spent on renovating this, and it would then be sent to London, where I should no doubt find it as serviceable as the other. I remembered the florally inlaid horror at Holt End, with its brass candlesticks and fretwork and hollow sound, and hastened north to prevent the catastrophe. I was too late.

A'ntie Ada's piano stood in the kitchen at Mount Road. Thirty pounds of my parents' savings had been spent on a renovation which they understood to have included new dampers and new felt on the hammers.

I played a few chords without pedal. The notes went on sounding. I took the front panel out. So far as I could see, all that the man had done for his thirty pounds was rub chalk on the felts. I did not discover who the man was. If I had pressed the question too hard, I could not have failed to reveal to my father how thoroughly he had been cheated. I tried to give the impression that everything was all right.

In December, a van from Hinderholme appeared in Pitt Rise. Late on a cold afternoon, A'ntie Ada's piano was impelled through the doorway in our little road by two enormous Yorkshiremen and one of moderate size, who was rather old.

Piano-removal is a specialised art, and these men were not specialists. At the turning in the stairs, we stuck. Wedged between the banisters and the low ceiling, the whole weight of A'ntie Ada's piano rested on the stomach of the smallest man, who was pinned against the wall. The four of us heaved without effect.

The men asked me to go out into the street and get hold of the first passer-by. Ignorant of London ways, they no doubt imagined that passers-by there carry about with them the same fund of general goodwill as may be expected from passers-by in Hinderholme. However, I went out into the drizzling twilight.

I should have gone as far as the grocer's, where Blod enjoyed Welsh goodwill, but striding up the hill, pipe in mouth, was a primitive painter of my acquaintance, German by origin, who, though rosy and bearing every sign of rude health, is rather small. Meanwhile, at the turn of the stairs, that poor man's stomach muscles were enduring a quite excessive strain.

'Ask no questions,' I said, 'but come quickly.'

'I come,' said the primitive painter.

With his added force, we got the back of A'ntie Ada's piano resting on the banister and slid it upstairs, knocking very little plaster down.

I should not have minded the hard hammers and dreadful soundboard if the dampers had worked. After all, Mozart and Beethoven played on instruments with that tone. But I could not accustom myself to those confused and unquenchable echoes. Apart from teaching Erica Jo her notes again, the only use for a piano like that would have been in the way of neighbourly reprisals. I have been offered the loan of it for that purpose, but moving it again seemed too difficult. I myself don't have neighbour trouble.

I stayed only until the Sunday afternoon. My father seemed frail and old. His asthma hadn't bothered him much lately, but so many earlier nights of desperate coughing and breathlessness had consumed him. It wasn't much of a life. After working a bit too hard for over fifty years, it seemed miserable to end without beer and smoking too few cigarettes.

A lot of hard-working men die very soon after their retirement. I'd read that in newspapers. What they're supposed to need is a new interest. My father had always been a handicrafts man, and I was spending far too much of the salary Matthew Latimer's paid me on getting my French books bound. I tried to interest my father in book-binding. Through old Matthew, I ought to be able to buy the essential presses and sewing frame cheap. My father clearly didn't feel like taking up anything new.

That last station was Cemmaes Road. The train climbs slowly between new afforestations. This must be Montgomeryshire.

The two men from Birmingham have just passed along the corridor again on the way back to their compartment. They didn't look in. When their shadow fell a few minutes ago, I rather expected some attempt by nudging and staring to put me out of countenance. I suppose the open exercise book and the spectacles and the fountain pen struck them as a fair enough alibi. They might think I was doing my accounts. I am, in a way.

ODD, HOW MY RHINELAND PILGRIMAGES SHOULD AT once thereafter involve me with my father again. But that is looking for coincidence and a pattern. There've only been two such pilgrimages, and this time there is no causal connection of a natural kind. The only conceivable link would be metaphysical.

Last time, it was Pargeter's fault. That was already more than twelve years ago. I was stranded in Brussels. The fare to London had been more francs than I had left. Brussels had been as far as I could book.

I wrote to several people. The others sent good advice and sympathy, but no money or a negligible amount. Pargeter sent eight pounds. But half of this he had got from my father. I was furious. I would rather have had four pounds and none from my father. If I had been willing to ask my father for money, I could have done so without intermediary.

During those years, I had kept up no connection with my parents, even by letter. I don't know that I ever thought of sparing them anxiety, though I would not willingly have caused them any. I was desperately hard-up, but my pride would never have let me write home for money. There was no spare money at home. Again, I don't know that I ever said this to myself, but, if anything, I ought to have been sending my parents money. The main thing was that I did not want their eye upon my life at all. Pargeter had never met my parents, did not live in Hinderholme, must have gone to the Registrar's office at the university to get my address.

In my time at Leeds, he had been an Oxford Grouper. Getting things right with his parents had been the chief problem Jesus (or whatever the Buchmanites call *Ah Lawd*) had helped him to solve. Possibly he wanted to force a show-down between my parents and me, under the impression that it would do us all good. Not that Pargeter had any reason to know what my relations with my parents were.

There'd been an exchange of letters during the winter. He knew about my conversion. He gave my father the address of Fr. Arbuthnot. Not long after my return to England, I had a letter from Fr. Arbuthnot, from which it appeared that *he* had had a letter from my father. He urged me to do all I could to reassure my father, who sounded so devoted to me.

At the end of March, my father turned up in London before eight o'clock one morning, having travelled by train from Hinderholme overnight. The directors at the Co-op had paid his fare so that he could visit the *Daily Mail* Ideal Home Exhibition, which might give him new ideas to place before the customers in Molethorpe.

There was not much furniture in the flat. My father sat on the edge of a divan bed. We exchanged a few polite commonplaces about the health of A'ntie Ada, A'ntie Beulah, Arthur, Uncle Nathan, A'ntie Ruth and Uncle Jim Brierley at Thongskirk.

My father tried to come to the point by asking:

'Is it a woman, lad?'

To some extent, it was.

'I suppose you could say it was,' is how I framed my reply.

'Are you going to have to marry her?' said my father.

That was easy.

'No,' said I, 'she wouldn't marry me.'

My poor father. The way he'd been brought up, trouble over a woman meant one thing. I did not for a moment imagine that this pale, anxious man, who now

sat on the edge of my bed in darkest Bohemia, had ever
himself put a girl in the family way before he married,
had ever been faced with a 'bun do' like Arthur Lumb.

I had contrived not to tell a direct lie. The whole
exchange was simply meaningless, as had been all our
exchanges for many years.

My mother was well. Indeed, she had taken a new
lease of life. Her energy was boundless. On Sunday
afternoons, she walked my father to death. During the
week, she went to meetings of the Women's League of
Health and Beauty and performed exercises on the
floor of the Drill Hall in Hinderholme. Clearly, this
was good news, but, as he told it to me, tears came into
my father's eyes, a thing I had never seen.

It may have been that, while he was telling it to me,
there had come into his mind a realisation that the
expected moment of truth between father and son
would not take place. I saw it rather as the acknow-
ledgment of weakness and failure. Late-developing
energy in women can crush a man who has not done
what he meant to do in life. I have seen a good deal of
this since. I did not understand it with perfect clarity
at that time. That is the sense, however, in which I
took my father's tears. And, indeed, although she has
spent the last nine years with one leg in irons, my
mother seems likely to survive my father.

I went with him to the *Daily Mail* Ideal Home
Exhibition. We ate baked beans on toast at a Lyons'
teashop. I was able to reassure him a bit. My position
at that moment was pretty good. I was just off to stay
with a publisher in Cornwall. I had a book with
photographs coming out in June.

There was some affection between my father and myself, but no real communication, no means of demonstrating affection. Neither of us could, in even the simplest way, help the other. I was embarrassed. I dare say my father was. I was glad to see him go. I dare say he was glad to be gone.

The year after that, I married old Flowerface. That was at the end of February, 1937.

From my father-in-law, I had £10. My parents bought me a new typewriter. The wedding was at Islington Town Hall.

I suppose that it was the *Daily Mail* Ideal Home Exhibition which brought my father to London that year, too. I kept out of the way, leaving him and his new daughter-in-law together. I met my father-in-law about five weeks later. This meeting also took place in London. Idwal John, J.P., was a huge, handsome Welshman, the very noblest type of provincial worthy, a voice of mercy on his local bench.

Just after that, King George VI was crowned. Blod and I being away at the time, my parents used our rooms. A'ntie Ada and Uncle Arthur Quarmby stayed at a hotel nearby.

That winter, I was in Hinderholme for a few days. This was to do with something I was writing, some journalistic kind of thing. After that, nothing until the outbreak of war.

The accident took place on the first night of the black-out. That was a few days before the outbreak. My mother was knocked down, stepping into the road at Folly Brig, by the sixty-foot trailer of an R.A.F. lorry. She lay there for some time before any passer-by noticed. Then foolish, well-meaning hands dragged her to safety, across the pavement and into the confectioner's and tobacconist's shop.

She lay in the Royal Infirmary for months, with a compound, splintered fracture that would not heal. My father wrote to me. I did not go home, and I wrote unsympathetically to him, because I detected a whining in his tone.

It was during this period that he developed asthma. I interpreted this on fashionable lines as a blackmailing attempt to compel his wife to come back home. I did not think of it as an attempt to compel me home. Perhaps it was. To that extent, I was perhaps responsible for that dreadful breathlessness, If I am dragged in chains before the Judgment Seat, it will be things like that rejection of my father which I shall have to answer for. The asthma did not subside when my mother came home with her leg in irons.

That made two of the womenfolk with their legs in irons. A'ntie Beulah's leg had been in irons since she fell off a 'bus at the stop in Bradford Road. Then Uncle Nathan Haigh, her husband, had a fall and was put to bed and died. Then A'ntie Beulah fell ill and was brought to Mount Road, to die at her brother's.

Once we had moved down into Ellen Brig, my father had the best part of a mile to walk uphill to the Shop. When I was there at the week-end in 1944, he came home late even on Saturdays. His normal working day seemed to be from eight in the morning until between eight and nine at night. Turned sixty, my father clearly felt that, if he did not, under war-time conditions and without a male assistant, shoulder the utmost that could have been expected of a younger man, he would be asked to go as soon as the war was over.

So there was all that anxiety, too, and even at the end his wages would not be more than six pounds a week. Though already a drapery branch manager, he'd married on two pounds a week. He'd left school at the age of twelve (since when, he said, he'd never read a book). The great chance for him seemed to lie at Carlin Beck, but after two years he'd been drawn back to Hinderholme by my mother's entreaties (and mine). Thereafter, he'd seen me through four more years at school and four at the university, and, as soon as I'd qualified, I left home and, so far as he could see, threw away all that specialised training. Marjorie'd spent only two years at a training college, and she stayed at home until this year.

Now he lies fighting for his breath in a darkened room, a man frail, grey and consumed. Through that rectangular hole in the wall, ventilating the box-room, failure, not a boggart, gibbers down upon his turning head. In every direction, his life stretches aridly about him. Dying, he lies abandoned in some Arizona of the mind.

It was not much of a life. Let death come easy. O God, give my father an easy death.

I said it aloud.

In a third-class carriage crossing Wales, I have just heard my own voice saying:

'O God, it was a hard life! Give him an easy death!'

The *globus hystericus* is in my throat. My eyes prickle. I am pleased with myself for being so moved.

This is Welshpool. Change here, then again at Shrewsbury.

The train bore right in a wide sweep past Staley-bridge, turning east into the Pennines. A brick land-scape has turned into a stone one. People's voices have taken on something of the quality of stone.

There were consolations. When I went home to-wards the end of the war, the vine in its thermostati-cally controlled, electrically heated greenhouse was new to me. It had a kind of symbolic identity. On Sunday morning and on late evenings in summer, my father lived its life. Men skilled with their hands can never be totally excluded from life. Pleased absorption is a form of happiness.

The furniture he made when he was young was never much to speak of aesthetically, but it was strong and durable. In the early years of the war, Blod took Erica Jo to Hinderholme. They liked that. Later, Marjorie fetched Erica Jo to stay in Hinderholme while Blod had Lewis at the nursing home in Devon-shire. Then my parents took Erica Jo back to Ex-minster and stayed for a week, very happily indeed, never having known any part of the southern country-side.

By that time, I was abroad again. In between, during the period when I was able to go home at the week-end, my relations with my father were all that they should have been.

On Saturday evening, he and I would go round to the

Woolpack. In my first days in the Army, I had had mittens and balaclavas and cigarettes out of a fund subscribed to by those old men. We talked to the old men and the fat barmaid who was the landlord's daughter-in-law and whose husband was in Persia. At a little after nine, one of us would go home and the other round to the chip-shop in Ellen Brig. On Sunday morning, there was always something to be done in the garden or greenhouse or in the allotments beyond.

Nothing very interesting would be said, but I became aware, as I had never consciously been, of the essential sweetness of the man. It seemed to me then, and seems now, astonishing how little I had succeeded in loving my father after the age of ten.

I had, I suppose, at one time feared him. If I now experienced fear through him, it was on account of his weakness. Without rancour, he was yet a disappointed and a wounded man. His face, sufficiently handsome but without boldness, had set in weak lines of disappointment.

He was not strong, of course, but he *was* handsome. His features were good, his mouth and eyes sensitive, the cold blue eyes wide-set. His gait was a bit odd, the feet much turned out, the knees giving, but he was tall, five feet eleven he said, tall enough for a bobby. I am less tall. His features were better, though my expression is bolder. It is him I take after, not my mother.

It is odd we should both have a scar on the top lip. He got his playing hide-and-seek in a hayfield. The boy who was It came looking for him with a hayfork. That was before they moved into Hinderholme.

Even when his pale-red moustache was bigger, you

noticed the scar if you looked closely where the moustache was parted, just over the lip-line. One of my earliest memories must be sitting athwart my father's lean thighs, playing with his watch-chain, ruffling his quiff, picking flattened dog-ends out of his waistcoat pockets, being 'whiskered' by him. I saw the scar then and was told about the hayfork.

I should be three at the time. The war must already have begun.

The blackened stone walls of a railway cutting rise sharply across the windows. With a scream, the train tears into the long tunnel under the Pennines.

I suppose that the other tunnel, through which the canal runs, lies to my right. How far away I don't know, perhaps just on the other side of that wall. They would make one operation of it all, or, if the railway came later, they would enlarge the original bore. The canal had no tow-path, and so the men had to lie on their backs and propel the barges by pushing with their feet against the tunnel roof. I don't suppose they do it now, but there were still 'leggers' all through my schooldays, at it for more than three suffocating miles.

Now we're out into the Hinder valley. Looking back, I can see the entrance to the canal tunnel, to the right. The railway clings to the high ground, canal and river both seeming to fall increasingly below it, the stone mill-chimneys, square or hexagonal, barely rising to the height of the carriage-windows. I remember these great square mills best at dusk in winter, their myriad lights twice reflected in canal and river.

On both sides of this viaduct, I look down into Thwaite. My father worked there during the four years before we moved to Carlin Beck. I can't see the road in which the Shop stood.

Again, a cutting rises steeply across the window. By the time the train has finished screaming, we shall be slowing down into Hinderholme station.

There were some trolley-buses before I left home in the first place, but I think there were still trams on this route during the war. At any rate, it seemed odd to purr smoothly down Folly Hill, instead of rocking and clanging as the driver braked hard, blue flashes at the wheels and at the hissing trolley. At the bottom, my mother lay half-conscious in the gutter, while an R.A.F. lorry drove on in cheerful ignorance, its trailer swaying, on the first night of the black-out, nine years ago.

I got off at the Mount, turned up past the chapel where my sister was married, left again by the school she went to when she was five and taught at when she was twenty, then right into this short, steep, curving road. The curtains were drawn, both upstairs and down. That ought to mean a death in the house, but the neighbours had not drawn their curtains on either side.

They might be drawn because my father lay in bed downstairs. I opened the passage door and went through to the back porch. There were bed-clothes blowing on the line. In the kitchen, wearing a flowered frock, my mother stood tearless with a visitor, who wore her best clothes. I knew her by sight.

There was an exchange of civilities. Then the visitor said, well, she'd better be going.

'I expect,' she said, 'Harold'll be wanting to see his father.'

And that was all. I had still been told nothing when I went through the front room and upstairs, though a sort of gulp began to take possession of my lungs as I went through the front room.

There he lay, in the small front bedroom, very beautiful, his features waxen and still, not wholly deprived of colour. At his neck, as though he were some French academician or diplomat, there was a silly, ceremonial, miniature come-to-Jesus collar and made-up white tie, undertaker's stage properties. I did not know which of the two opposing impulses was the more self-conscious and theatrical, the desire now at last to kiss my father's well-formed mouth or that fear of the dead which kept me from doing so.

It was at about nine o'clock on Monday that he had collapsed in the kitchen. It had been a 'stroke'. He died this morning, in the small hours, about four o'clock. By the time I left Aberystwyth, he had been dead already some nine hours. He had been dead four hours when I got my sister's telegram this morning.

The strange thing was that A'ntie Jean had also collapsed with a 'stroke' at about the same time of the evening, two days before, on Saturday, in our kitchen. At first, she was put to bed where my father now lies, in the small front bedroom. When he collapsed, she had to be moved. She was moved to what used to be the Workhouse, next door to Linfootlock Council School, where I spent the first seven of my years at school.

Because Grandad Sykes drank, my mother's family always feared to find themselves in the Workhouse.

34

My father's death has been kept from A'ntie Jean, and it appears that she rages incoherently with resentment against her sister, my mother, who sent her away to die in the Workhouse. Of course, it is no longer a poor-law institution but a municipal, as during my earliest school days it was a military, hospital. To A'ntie Jean in her stricken condition, the change of status seems unconvincing.

One is accustomed to imitative crimes and 'waves' of suicides. It is difficult to see mere coincidence in these two parallel calamities. There must, I feel, at least have been 'suggestion' of a kind. It is all a bit eerie.

Visits of condolence have been going on intermittently all evening, since a late high tea. Each caller, before his departure, has to be asked whether he wants to 'see' my father.

There is some local custom according to which you say:

'Touch him, and go.'

Apart from the quiet presence upstairs, the atmosphere in the house is perfectly normal. My mother wears her customary brave smile. Marjorie has behaved throughout with a competence I could not hope to emulate. They will sleep together in the big front-bedroom. I shall have my old room at the back.

II

THIS IS THE EARLIEST PHOTOGRAPH. UNTIL A'NTIE
Beulah got married, it used to stand over the piano in
Waterside Lane.

My father will be about ten, so the photograph must
have been taken in the early 'nineties, just after the
family had moved into Hinderholme. That must be a
Co-op horse, and the background will be the stables
behind Waterside Lane.

Grandad Atha, holding the head of the horse on
which young Alfred, not yet my father by almost
twenty years, sits, is a little man, bow-legged, with a
drooping moustache which seems already white. He
stares defiantly into the eye of the camera, perhaps the
first he saw. I barely remember him, and I am not sure
that I remember Grandma Atha at all, though I have
some notion of a tall woman, white-haired and pretty
in a fragile way. I do remember myself being held,
presumably by my father, on the back of a mountainous
dappled-grey horse, of which I fancy my grandfather
held the head, in that long, cobbled stableyard by the
dye-polluted, boulder-strewn waters of the Hinder.

Although it lies in a southerly part of the town, that

must still be the Hinder. The Helm joins it, I fancy, not much more than two hundred yards further on to the south-east, under the road where the Molethorpe trams turn off at the top of Folly Hill. Turned off.

The horse on which young Alfred Atha sits, of a uniform colour neither very light nor very dark in tone, is not the heaviest type of carthorse, but more like a Suffolk punch and presumably of much the colour it appears to have in a sepia photograph. Alfred o' Judd's or Fred o' Judd's, he once told me, was my father's name while he still lived in the country beyond Cowl Hill, but perhaps at the time of the photograph he was already known by his registered surname, as Fred or Alfred Atha, Judd Atha's or George Atha's lad. He wears long black stockings, an Eton collar, a cap with a button. There would already be the scar on his top lip.

There are no other photographs of him as a boy. He next appears with a moustache, fuller than I recall, twisted, presumably waxed, at the ends, his front hair brushed up in a quiff. He is hollow-cheeked, and his pale eyes protrude more than it seems to me they ever did later.

He must already have been in his late twenties, drapery manager at the Ellen Brig branch of the Hinderholme Co-operative and Industrial Society, singing tenor in the choir at Hoyland Street, where he met Ethel Sykes. She, my mother, with dark, piled-up hair, high-necked white blouse, hands folded in the lap of a dark skirt, looks rather beautiful, though I suppose her teeth were already false. Her expression is severe, though she insists that in those days she was known as a bright-eyed smiler. My father was always over-serious.

There is something here of a hunted-gazelle look in the eyes, though I suppose gazelles all have brown eyes. My mother's eyes were green-flecked hazel.

They must already have been engaged, my mother still working at the wholesale stationer's. In the wedding photograph, neither is much changed. That frock coat and top hat were still kept in the wardrobe at the first house I lived in.

That was in Radcliffe Road, Linfootlock, a westerly part of the town, not yet built up, still encroaching on moorland rising into the Pennines between the two valleys of the Helm and Hinder. Even the front road was still unmetalled. Quartz particles glittered in the new stone. The row was stepped every three or four houses, and on that side of the street, facing the sun, two passages had been left for the general convenience, the row being sufficiently long. That house stood below the higher, more westward passage, and so its upstairs premises, lying over the passage, were a good yard wider than the average.

There were two rooms downstairs, two and a lavatory up, a cellar and a coal-cellar below. The front garden was small, the back garden longer, so that, away from the house, towards the gate, the sun reached it much of the day, if there was sun.

Across the road at the front were similar houses. Across the road at the back were back-to-back houses, with their outdoor privies on that side. This made for social difference, though, soon after their honeymoon at Morecambe, my not-quite-yet parents made friends with the two families most directly opposite at the back, the one slightly to the left already having two sons, aged five and eight. Those were the Mellors. The Dysons, a little to the right, were childless and would remain so.

For the eighteen or so years of photographic black-out, I know only that, at the age of twelve, my father had first gone to work as a flour-boy at the Co-op and that later he worked in drapery at the Central for some years before he became a branch manager. I know what both facts mean. Until twenty years ago, most of the women in this neighbourhood still baked their own bread. My mother baked bread on Tuesdays at least until I left home fourteen years ago. When I was ten or eleven, I fetched stones of flour in a white cotton bag with a blue-and-white checked flour cloth knotted about it. At every Co-op grocery branch, there was a flour room at the back, the walls lined with square zinc bins out of which different qualities of flour were shovelled with a tin scoop. Keeping the women's bags filled was a job for one white-overalled man and a boy. At the Central, you had to do with furniture, linoleum and hardware.

All my father's family worked at the Co-op, once they had moved into Hinderholme. Grandad Atha was a 'teamer'. This, I suppose, meant both that he drove carts and that he groomed horses in the stables behind Waterside Lane. My father's sister, A'ntie Beulah, who was ten years older than he, worked at the Co-op restaurant, of which, by the time I distinctly remember her, she had risen to be manageress.

I was conceived, no, not at Morecambe, but two months or more after my parents' return from their honeymoon, in the autumn of 1910. I was born the following summer in a heat-wave, under a Liberal government, in the first year of a new reign.

There is one photograph of me at a few months old, enormously fat in a long frock. Here, I must be three, possibly four, years old. I wear boots, stockings gartered below the knee, short trousers and a kind of sailor's tunic without piped calico, cotton or linen collar over the navy-blue serge. I am standing up very straight on a photographer's stool, my hands behind my back. My face is so fat, the eyes are mere slits, and my nose barely projects enough to afford air-vent through my nostrils.

Here, I scowl in a group snapshot. There, I carry a model sailing-boat. But for those years I have memories already. My father is a real physical presence. I have sat across his thighs and ruffled his hair. He has parted his knees to drop me, then at once caught me and laughed.

The house itself was a physical presence. In most households, that back room would have been the kitchen, but at Radcliffe Road we called it the scullery, perhaps because both my parents had been brought up in back-to-back houses, without kitchens. The mat by the door was up for shaking. Most of the concrete floor was covered with coconut matting. I sat by the door.

'Don't sit down on t' concrete, Harold lad,' said my mother. 'It'll strike a chill.'

It did, too. It was lovely. As soon as her back was turned, I tried it again, letting the concrete strike its chill through the seat of my trousers, then standing up and feeling my bottom grow delightfully warm again.

That is my first distinct memory. My second concerns

a trick of memory itself. This again was in the scullery. Toys were kept on a broad shelf, above where the zinc bath hung. Standing on a tall buffet to get something down, I have discovered toys whose existence I had forgotten. I shall not remember what particular toys they were, but, when I have finished playing with them and my mother is putting them away, I tell her to put them right at the back, so that I can forget about them again.

BOTH MARJORIE AND I HAVE ANSWERED THE FRONT DOOR to florists' boys with large bunches of gladioli. The last time the bell went, my sister let somebody in.

Our mother was out at the back, either collecting or pegging out further bed-clothes on the line and talking to the nice wife of the deaf young man next door above. Whoever Marjorie let in had gone upstairs. Marjorie herself came into the kitchen, where I was sitting (as I now am again) in the chair by the shoe-cupboard, with the cardboard box of small albums and photographs and my exercise book.

Marjorie said:

'Will you stop Mother coming in for a while? They're bringing Dad downstairs.'

I went out on to the small raised lawn, which I had re-levelled with my father's help one Saturday evening during the war. I had dug up the turf, and my father had stacked it. I had filled the wheelbarrow with soil, and my father had tipped the barrowloads towards the subsided edge. We laid the spirit-level on a clothes prop, one of the two, normally kept along iron hooks in the passage, used to hold up the line on which the freshly washed sheets now blew. This is a sunny morning. It is Friday. The funeral is to-morrow.

It was not difficult to keep my mother engaged in conversation out at the back. I did not really know the nice wife (or, indeed, the deaf husband), and so there were formalities and civilities to go through.

Among the local death stories, some depend on the difficulty of bringing coffins round a corner in narrow stairs. No doubt to-day they placed the coffin where it now stands in the front room and brought my father downstairs in the wing collar, white tie, dickie and winding sheet. Certainly, it would have been a shocking sight, especially to a wife or, as she now is, a widow.

The trimmings of death seem unnecessarily tiresome. Why cannot one simply bury one's dead in one's own back garden, if one has a back garden? By all means, let a man from the Borough Surveyor's come round and see that the grave is deep enough and clear of the water supply. The State compels one to deal with those dreadful gentlemen in top hats, who are nevertheless left free to organise the matter to their private advantage. Perhaps it was industries like this which Mr Attlee and his colleagues should have nationalised in the first place. The *pompes funèbres*, some of the things solicitors do such as house-conveyancing, lotteries, pawnbroking. Abroad, most of these things have always been nationalised, like the mines and the railways.

At any rate, there the coffin now stands on low trestles, the lid screwed down, by the window behind drawn curtains. The mahogany table, on which at various times fern, aspidistra or small palm stood during a period of thirty-eight years, has been moved into the corner. The mounting gladioli are kept fresh in buckets beside the coffin.

The table here stood in the front room at Radcliffe Road. So did the treadle sewing-machine now also kept in here. So did the piano. So did the music-holding piano buffet and the music cabinet, both made by my father. The glass-fronted cupboard in the back room upstairs was also the work of his hands. So was the box for boot-cleaning materials in the back porch. The gate-legged table now kept here in the kitchen stood only briefly in the front room at Radcliffe Road, was bought in about 1921, at a time when the house had already been wired for electricity by my father and when a Mr Kershaw no longer called for the rent on Monday mornings, because the house was being bought through a building society.

This sliding armchair and the one facing, at my mother's end of the table, were bought after we came here, a mere twenty years ago. Cushions from the Chesterfield suite in the front room (bought at Carlin Beck) have been placed in the bottom of this one, I don't know why.

My mother comes in, through the porch. I ask her. She says:

'That's the chair Dad collapsed in. He wet it through. It's got to be re-covered.'

Damn, I ought not to have asked. But my mother is being very matter-of-fact. My brother-in-law, George Binns, is coming over from Warrington this evening. He will stay in the house to-night and to-morrow night.

44

He and Marjorie are to have the big front bedroom. My mother will sleep in the bed just now vacated by my father. I do not think I should have cared to sleep there yet.

The deaf young man next door is to have my father's diamond glass-cutter. My mother hopes I shan't mind. The young man had often borrowed the glass-cutter, and he wanted something to remember Dad by.

More gladioli. This afternoon, I think I will go up to Linfootlock and see whether Radcliffe Road has much changed. I have also volunteered to go up to Holt End and let Arthur know what the funeral arrangements are for to-morrow.

FROM THE FRONT, YOU CAN SEE COWL HILL WITH ITS Victorian watch-tower, at a thousand feet. A bit more than half-way up the Scar towards Molethorpe, you can also see Tenpetty Row and the house we lived in first after we came back from Carlin Beck.

I walk down the front steps, turn right to the bottom of Mount Road, turn right for a hundred yards along Albert Road, right again into Ram Lane, at a point a hundred or so yards above the near end of Ellen Brig and the Shop my father had just become drapery manager at when he got married. In later years, whenever I walked this way, I followed Ram Lane all the way, until, as it bore sweepingly right past the main entrance to the engineering works, it changed its name and came out on to the tramlines past the church school. Now, after I have walked under the railway bridge, I turn right through a ginnel and come into a cinder track past what used to be the Wreck.

This brings you out by the bakehouse, built when I was about ten. You turn left into Radcliffe Road and cross over to what was our side.

The roadway is metalled now. In my childhood, the rain washed sand into crinkled patterns along the gutter.

You are walking at a gentle slope uphill and, I suppose, west-north-west by west, away from the centre of Hinderholme. The front gardens of all these houses are very small, but they get plenty of sun.

From this point onward (*i.e.* from just below the bottom passage), with one or two hesitations between the two passages, I could reel off the names of all the families who lived on this side of Radcliffe Road to some way above the top passage and, indeed, with only one or two further gaps, to the very top of the street, between thirty and twenty-five years ago. I slow up as I come to the house Brian Solace lived in. Then came 'Grandma' Walker's. Then us. Then the passage and 'Grandma' Booth's. But the passage has been closed up.

It has a separate door, so that the house we lived in cannot have been structurally altered inside, but the space now clearly belongs to that house. It must be of some advantage to the people who live there, but an inconvenience to people on the other side of the road.

I wonder what sort of people live there. It is still quite a respectable little road.

If I knocked at the door and some rather grim, un-intelligent-looking woman appeared, I should have to say:

'Please forgive me, I lived here as a child, when the

house was new. I suppose you wouldn't let me just peep inside. . . .'

It couldn't be done, and I don't know where else I could knock to find out what sort of people lived in that house. Certainly, there are no Solaces, Walkers or Booths. There were no families elsewhere in the road with whom my parents kept up relations later. I mustn't hang around, or heads behind lace curtains will speculate.

There are flowers of some kind, but not love-lies-bleeding. The Dorothy Perkins climbing rose which framed that window has been cut down and uprooted.

It was along that turning off the other side of the road that Sylvia Jagger lived. She must have been five before me. I went to her party. There was kiss-on-the-cushion, postman's knock and trifle. Sylvia Jagger had golden ringlets, a black velvet hair-band and a pink sash. My love-life began with Sylvia Jagger.

After Easter, we both started going to school. Greta Jagger took us. Greta Jagger was seven. She was in Standard One, Ma Wrigley's class, and could read. The way to school was up here, then right and left round the allotments, then right to the tramlines and left. I'll go that way. I'll go as far as the school. I can walk down Radcliffe Road back street on the way home.

No allotments now, of course, or, I suppose, these twenty-eight years. These, at the corner, the bottom of what became Church Street East, would be the first of Law Barraclough's buildings, going up very slowly during the war. He lived just across there, with his carts and hand-carts on a patch of brick-strewn waste ground against the gable-end of the row.

There were, I think, four houses, and their walls had not yet risen more than two or three feet above the foundations. One evening, on the way home from school, Sylvia Jagger and I went behind the low walls and showed each other our bottoms. Mrs Barraclough saw us and told our mothers. The Barracloughs had no children.

It would be on a Saturday morning when I fell off Law Barraclough's cart on the patch of waste ground. Or, rather, I did not fall off. I was catapulted off.

We swung on the shafts of a cart until they came down to the ground. We then climbed on to that end of the cart. Our combined weight kept it depressed. Suddenly, Brian Solace, Sylvia Jagger and the rest, as though at a prearranged signal, jumped off. The force of gravity promptly restored the cart to its normal position, and I was thrown as if out of a ballista, landing on my head among the stones. Mothers were run for, and I was carried home unconscious. My head was bleeding, but the harm was in fact slight, and Dr Holroyd put no stitches in. Perhaps you can't put stitches in a head, because of the bone.

The allotments covered all that area in front of me and to the left, now occupied by three, perhaps even four, streets. My father's allotment would be fifty or a hundred yards in, towards the middle but a bit this way. His greenhouse was the biggest in the field, big enough for allotment holders' meetings, big enough for the annual show. His yellow tomatoes and his chrysanthemums at Christmas were unrivalled.

Until I was nine or ten, my father and I spent alternate Sunday mornings in the allotments. Law Barraclough's allotment stood next to my father's, separated from it by a neat turf wall. As if to presage a post-war boom in building, the spring sun of 1919 brought Law Barraclough's peas up faster than my father's, though Law Barraclough was not much of a gardener.

I was seven and in Standard Two. That Sunday morning, my father and Law Barraclough stood side by side on the latter's grass path. I fidgeted near them, for it was dinner-time, and it would be no use as late as this asking for another young turnip to peel and eat. Law Barraclough was a red-faced, domineering, clean-shaven man, much shorter than my father.

My father chewed his moustache with grief. There was no doubt about it. His peas were up barely an inch. Law Barraclough's stood nearly three inches high.

'You know, lass,' said my father, as he carved the roll of brisket for our Sunday dinner that day, 'Law Barraclough's peas are up three times as far as mine.'

My mother's tone indicated that the wrongs committed by Law Barraclough extended far beyond the disgracefully rapid growth of his peas. If it came to that, I too had once suffered injury, if not at the hands of Law Barraclough, yet as a result of playing on one of his carts.

On Monday afternoon, I came home from school with Sidney Sapworth, a notoriously wild class-mate who had curly yellow hair, a nose already prominently bridged (in contrast with the small buttons most of us wore on the front of our faces) and a lone-handed, unaccountable temper. It was not usual for me to walk home with Sidney Sapworth, who lived down by the Fullers' Arms and had no occasion to turn off the main road at this point. I doubt whether Sidney Sapworth had seen the allotments before or knew of their existence.

'Yon big greenhouse is me Dad's,' I told him.

I led Sidney Sapworth along the main allotment path and showed him. As the greenhouse was locked, I could not take him in. We peered through the glass. I pointed out the stove and the pipes all round to keep the place warm in winter, the tomato plants and the half-hardy annuals for bedding out.

Sidney Sapworth noticed the contrasted rows of peas on either side of the sod wall.

'What's them?' he said, 'Peas?'

I recalled my father's dissatisfaction and Law Barraclough's grave fault in causing it.

'Your Dad's aren't as big as this lot, are they?' said Sidney Sapworth.

Now my pride was touched, as well as my sense of justice.

'Let's transplant 'em,' I said.

'What's that mean?' said Sidney Sapworth.

'Put me Dad's peas where Law Barraclough's is, and Law Barraclough's here.'

The suggestion undoubtedly came from me. At the same time, the idea might not have occurred to me if Sidney Sapworth had not been there. He was sly, daring and turbulent. I wanted to vie with him.

It was twilight. There seemed to be nobody about. Sidney Sapworth and I began systematically transplanting the seedlings from Law Barraclough's allotment to my father's and *vice versa*, dibbling them in with our forefingers and doubtless breaking the roots.

'Nobody'll see us if we keep us heads down,' I said.

But I had counted without the all-seeing eye and all-reporting tongue of Mrs Barraclough.

We had almost finished when I heard voices approaching through the now deeper dusk. Incredibly, they were the voices of my father and Mr Barraclough. Sidney Sapworth and I made ourselves small and crouched hopelessly against the sod wall, in the corner, by a heap of weeds and old roots stacked for burning. I can smell them now.

While Law Barraclough and my father inspected the damage, Sidney Sapworth fled. Law Barraclough maintained an impressive and menacing silence. My father chewed his moustache.

I walked home with my father.

'Nay, Harold lad,' he said, 'I wish it hadn't ha' been Law Barraclough.'

I am certain I made no attempt to put the blame on Sidney Sapworth, though he, in the ordinary way, was no more a friend of mine than Law Barraclough was of my father's. It was my father who decided I had been led astray. He told me to keep away from Sidney Sapworth in future, and that was the only punishment I got. Although I had painfully humiliated him in the sight of Law Barraclough, my father saw clearly that I had meant to do him a service.

That was the last time I had any personal dealings with Law Barraclough, apart from the occasion when he called out behind Peter Holmes and me and went unanswered. He grew rich and, a year or so after the incident of the pea-seedlings, built himself a handsome bungalow in the fashionable area near Mallalieu Park, where even now Linfootlock barely encroaches upon the moorland. I always knew which house it was, and to see my new Uncle Gordon come out of it during the summer of the eclipse would have set me speculating without any further unusual circumstance.

Now right again into the main road and up left, where tramlines ran in a cobbled roadway. Past the point where following Ram Lane would have brought me out, the continuation of the road to my right passing the Wesleyans and then going down past the saw-mill into Thwaite.

You come first to the Workhouse gates, then Girls, then Infants, then Boys. The gates stand in a row, joined together by spiked iron railings of identical pattern and painted the same green. School and Workhouse must have been built at the same time, the playgrounds and the long concrete path to the Workhouse laid out in a single operation. Only the Infants' clock-towered, Gothically pinnacled building is fully visible from the road, cloistered coke-heaps and boiler-house lying under the flight of stone steps at the top of which Miss Wrigley stood to ring her bell. The main buildings lie behind, the Girls' and Boys' playgrounds separated by a high wall. What used to be the Workhouse stands further back still, now grouped among other hospital buildings.

Ma Wrigley was the Infants' headmistress. She looked it, thin and rigid in high-necked blue bombasine, a cameo brooch attaching the thin gold chain of her *pince-nez*. We formed up into not very satisfactory rows, and the Baby Class was marched off through the cloak-rooms (over there, to the right) by Miss Dudley, who was nice and pink and plump and quite young.

To date, I could neither read nor tell the time. After all, I was only four. But I did know my left hand from my right. Either Miss Dudley didn't, or she held mistaken views on how to teach. That conclusion I formed within half an hour on my first day at school.

We stood up in our desks and did arms bend, arms upward stretch, arms bend, arms downward stretch, arms bend, arms outward stretch, arms bend, arms forward stretch, arms bend, left arm outward stretch, bend, right arm outward stretch, bend, left arm. . . . At that point, I could bear it no longer. I stopped doing exercises and remained with my right arm upward stretched.

When I had received Miss Dudley's attention, I said:

'Please, Miss, when you're telling us to stretch us left arms, *you*'re stretching your right.'

'Well, in a way, that's true, Harold,' said Miss Dudley, but I want you to stretch the arm on the same side as I'm stretching on.'

Feeble, unprincipled, I thought. Likely enough to set up a lasting confusion in the minds of young children. However, as I was new, perhaps I had better not make an issue of it. So I went on doing what Miss Dudley wanted, protesting inwardly.

Exercises did not go on all day. There would be coloured paper shapes next or beads or rest your heads on your arms on the desk and don't look up till I say or sand-trays. In due course, the bell would go for playtime.

On the afternoon of my third day at school, I was glad I had not offended Miss Dudley. Sylvia Jagger had brought a note from her mother to leave early. Greta would be leaving early, too. They had not told me.

Miss Dudley said:

'Well, Sylvia, it's a quarter to four now. You'd better go.'

Urgently, I right arm upward stretched.

'Please, Miss,' I said, 'can *I* go an' all? I al'ays walk home with Sylvia Jagger and Greta.'

If Miss Dudley had been against me, it might have been awkward. I doubted very much whether I could have found the way home by myself.

When I could, Sylvia and I no longer waited for Greta. Greta was nice, but might not have lent herself to the revelation behind the walls of Law Barraclough's new buildings.

There were not only beads, paper shapes and sand-trays at school. There was also plasticine. Sylvia Jagger's bottom had scarcely blown over when I put a lump of plasticine in my pocket and took it home. In the evening, I brought it out and began to shape it into a rhinoceros.

'What's that, Harold lad?' said my mother. 'Plasticine?'

'Mm,' said I.

'Where'd it come from?' said my father. 'School?'

'Mm,' said I.

'Well, you'd better take it back, hadn't you?'

'That's stealing,' said my mother.

I put my rhinoceros down on the sheet of newspaper I had carefully spread on the table to protect the cloth.

'It'll save you brass,' I said.

'Nay, Harold lad,' said my father, 'if we want you to have plasticine, we s' buy it.'

'I won't have plasticine i' th' house,' said my mother. 'It's dirty stuff. It treads into t' carpet.'

'You must take it back to-morn, lad,' said my father.

'I should ha' thought you'd ha' been pleased,' I said.

'Nay, to think my son's a thief,' said my mother.

Taking it back would be awkward. Miss Dudley's cupboard was kept locked, and we might not have plasticine to-morrow.

'Can't I chuck it on t' fireback?' I said. 'They aren't short at school.'

At the Workhouse gates stood soldiers in hospital blues, some on crutches and some with an arm missing. We took them packets of cigarettes and asked them for the fag-cards. This we did rather than extract the cards first because some of the soldiers had told us that they saved fag-cards for children of their own.

Before Christmas in 1916, we gave a concert for the wounded soldiers at the Workhouse. I was in the Second Class. The Infants' contribution was a song. It went:

> I'm an airman, I'm an airman,
> And I fly, fly, fly, fly, fly. . . .

I suppose that the next line would be:

> . . .Up in the sky. . . .

And then, no doubt:

> . . . Ever so high. . . .

This song was sung by four boys of between five and seven, dressed in then not inappropriately khaki uniforms and forage caps. I was the youngest. The other three were in Standard One, Ma Wrigley's class.

I suppose the casual ward had been closed for the duration. This was hard on its regular customers, such as Itchy Coo. Every few weeks, Itchy was to be seen for a day or two loitering unhappily about the streets of Linfootlock, with his newspaper bundle and his wild grey beard, the fleas hopping off him in clouds.

By the summer of 1917, I had given Sylvia Jagger up. This was partly because I was teased for playing with girls, but it was not long before I let my affections wander to Mildred Walsh. After the holidays, I went up into Ma Wrigley's class. Mildred Walsh and I were two of the four good readers. The other two were a girl of Danish parentage called Karen and a boy with projecting teeth, Wilfred Helliwell, who lived up beyond the tram terminus by the quarries. Each of us sat with a group of the other children and taught them to read. Sylvia Jagger was not very clever. She took to wearing spectacles, and her hair turned a dull brown.

I was sandy-haired, pale and serious. I was on the fat side, though not grotesquely so. In that respect, I had every reason to suppose that my appearance would improve. In another respect, I was displeased with myself.

For my birthday, somebody had given me *The Queen's Gift Book*. This was not a children's book at all. It was a charitable compilation on behalf of the badly wounded, edited by John Galsworthy and with contributions from Joseph Conrad, Sir James Barrie, John Buchan, Jerome K. Jerome, 'Sapper' and Sir Arthur Conan Doyle, Ethel M. Dell and Mrs Humphrey Ward. There were coloured pictures by members of the Royal Academy. One showed a gun-team of sailors, with a ghostly Nelson in the sky. In another, a knight of the Crusades in full armour stood behind a living soldier, his hand on the shoulder of a dead one. Another showed the Prince of Wales in Garter robes, with black velvet cloak, two enormous, gilt-tasselled bell-pulls at his waist and white stockings. It was the legs in the stockings which fascinated me. I despaired of ever possessing such legs. My calves, I felt sure, would never swell out until they were the same breadth as my knees.

Because of a weak chest, my father was never called up into the Army, though, at various times, as the medical standard dropped, he expected to be. At one such time, we took in a lodger, Miss James, a clergyman's daughter from London, working as a draughtsman at the big engineering works off Ram Lane. She was diminutive and had red-gold hair. She designed chocolate-box lids (professionally, I think) and taught me a certain amount about drawing faces and painting in water colours. I confessed to her my envy of the Prince of Wales's legs. Miss James told me that they would not be the Prince's own legs at all, but that either another man would have posed for that part of the picture or the artist would have made them up out of his own head. This was some consolation.

At my request, Miss James did a portrait of herself in a cowboy hat. After the war, she and I were to be married and to live in Texas. But all that was at home. At school, my interest devolved on Mildred Walsh. I studied her legs in the playground. Among all the legs I knew (and I knew a great many), they alone were up to the pseudo-Prince's standard.

Not that Mildred Walsh's legs were by any means her only commendation. I liked her curiously pallid, sharp-toothed face. I always liked it. There came a time when I thought Mildred Walsh's legs exaggerated (and then another, later time when I did not), but I always liked her face. For eight years, at Linfootlock Council School, she and I were always in the same class, and, even during the two years when I was against girls and the one year during which she became unpopular as Jacko's pet, I still liked her face. I went on liking it for ten years after that, and I liked it when I saw it again after an interval of ten years, four years ago, during the war. It was a pale face. Mildred Walsh's skin was opaquely creamy, and, although she was perfectly healthy and even a rather athletic girl, no colour ever appeared in it, except a few indistinct freckles under the eyes in summer. There was a faded, sun-bleached quality about the colouring even of her eyes and hair.

She was no albino. The word 'albino' was unknown to the community in which I lived, but upon the fringes of that community a true albino did (if the word be thought applicable to such unfortunate people) flourish. He was the vicar of a church which catered for the spiritual needs of rather few of our neighbours and of whose whereabouts I was (and am) only vaguely aware, though he was also in some way superintendent of a C. of E. elementary school, to which, since it was nearer than this, went the children of some in Radcliffe Road and Springland Street who were, if anything, of nonconformist persuasion. He was simply described as having pink eyes, and it was known that his sermons and announcements had to be written out in huge black characters if he was to see them in church.

His house stood in the main road, further down than

I shall have to go before I turn off to get to Radcliffe Road back street. I don't know whether it is still there. It was masked by a privet hedge of exceptionally long-established growth, the tough, straight shoots from whose base made splendid bows and arrows.

Outside Wales, all Methodists are the same now. In those days, there were Primitive and United Methodists as well as Wesleyans, in Linfootlock. The small United chapel, here just below school, has been closed, and will no doubt be pulled down. I come to the point at which the main road is crossed by the continuation of Ram Lane coming in from the right and, to the left, the road past the Wesleyans which also, once he had left the Ellen Brig branch, took my father down past the saw-mill and to Thwaite. As the great planks met them, the saws shrieked and sobbed like pigs in a slaughterhouse.

The chapel, too, has its pinnacles, and there are laurels about it. I don't know whether I was christened here or at the chapel in town where my father sang tenor in the choir. After their marriage, my parents stopped going to chapel, but in due course I was sent to Sunday school here.

They soon had me performing. At some concert, I had to recite Thackeray's poem about a Chinaman who, for some reason, wanted his pigtail to hang in front.

> There lived a sage in days of yore,
> And he a handsome pigtail wore;
> But wondered much and sorrowed more,
> Because it hung behind him. . . .

No doubt I was made to turn round in imitation of the

Chinaman's frenzied efforts to get the pigtail to do what he wanted, but of this I cannot be sure. What I do remember is my blouse of champagne-coloured shantung silk. This was no part of an attempt to supply local colour. It was simply that I had been bought a blouse of shantung. I hated it. The champagne-coloured silk clung to my fingers and crackled electrically.

Mildred Walsh's parents were notables at the Wesleyans. Her mother was a school-teacher outside Linfootlock, her father an insurance man. At the Anniversary, Mildred and I were made to read the lessons.

When the organ started playing, she and I were sitting in the vestry with the circuit minister, Mr Hardcastle, a rich man with a white moustache. The organ changed its tune. Mr Hardcastle, Mildred Walsh and I emerged from the vestry in full view of a packed congregation all in their new spring clothes and climbed the steps into the broad pulpit, where Mildred and I sat at either end of the long seat covered with a single, narrow, red plush cushion. When my turn came, I moved forward to the huge, gilt-edged, big-printed Bible and pretended to read from its pages the psalm I in fact knew by heart.

My parents did come to chapel on that occasion. There sat my father in his new blue suit, his hair brushed up in a quiff, his reddish moustache, I fancy, no longer waxed, there, beside him, my mother in new hat and new brown costume, sniffing the Californian Poppy scent on a lace handkerchief, a bit red-eyed but otherwise behaving very well.

Now back to the main road. Left, past the point at which I should turn off for Church Street East. Right here and to the top of Springland Street.

Not much changed. The roadway here was always concrete. The houses to my left were not back-to-back houses, but those to the right were and are. The second house down was Freddie Fischer's. The next was Arthur Lumb's. The last time I walked down this street was twenty-three years ago. I saw Arthur Lumb then, but we did not speak.

Freddie Fischer's father was a German. He was interned in the Great War. He was an engineer. Arthur Lumb's father worked at the mill. He was older than most fathers. He wore a drooping white moustache, and he was very bow-legged. A lot of the older mill-workers were bow-legged.

Those were still the days of clogs and shawls. Early in the morning, there was a clip-clop of clogs even on causeways as genteel as those of our front road. Mr Lumb went out to work in blue overalls, cap and muffler, clogs, his dinner basin knotted in a red handkerchief.

Arthur Lumb was cock of the neighbourhood. He was not a bullying or even an aggressive boy. His features were good, his skin delicate, his movements oddly tremulous, as though his strength were an illness. His voice was light and soft, and, when he gave battle, he went into it with a sad, whinnying sound, blushing.

Sidney Sapworth once attacked Arthur Lumb in this street. Arthur Lumb picked Sidney Sapworth up, turned him upside down and, with a sigh which was almost a squeak, dropped him head first on that concrete roadway. I was once foolish enough to attack Arthur Lumb myself. That was in the Wreck. I went home very bloody. As my father pointed out, it served me right.

Arthur Lumb and Freddie Fischer were both a year or more older than me. They stayed on in Ma Webb's class and did not go to the Grange. At fourteen, they went out to work in caps and mufflers. By that time, Brian Solace, Leslie Balmforth and I were already committed to collar and tie.

This is still waste ground. I pass the tarred gable-end, much bounced-against by balls, chalked with a representation of cricket stumps, and come out into the back road opposite a point two doors up from where we lived. The houses on the left are in Springland Street. Those on the right are in Radcliffe Road.

The roadway here is still unmetalled. I remember it as a cinder road. Now, through a surface of indistinguishable substance but green with moss, project stones rounded like pebbles, which, I'd say, make it impassable to cars and tradesmen's vans.

It was never possible for two vehicles to cross in the back road. During the course of the day and especially in the morning, there was a slow, intermittent procession of milk carts, coal carts, greengrocers' carts, the rubbish cart, rag-and-bone men, the fish man, Co-op delivery carts and, once a week, the tub cart.

As seen from our back door, this procession moved from right to left, proceeding west-north-west and away from town, gently uphill. In the morning, one horse or another generally stood or plodded a few yards forward. Sometimes, a donkey suddenly brayed.

There was always a donkey on Friday. The fish cart was pulled by a donkey. The horses sometimes stood with their nose-bags on. They often dropped useful manure outside one's back gate. Less frequently, a great splashing was to be heard, and there arose the dreadful smell of horses' urine.

The rectangular superstructure of the tub cart was fitted with yellow tarpaulin, easily and commodiously raised at the side in sections. On the back were the stencilled letters 'H C S D'. These, we had unbelievingly been told, stood for 'Hinderholme Corporation *Sanitary* Department'. We had a song about the tub cart. It went:

> The Corporation muck cart
> Was full up to the brim;
> The Corporation driver
> Fell in and couldn't swim. . . .

It was odd, where the social dividing line ran. It might have been expected to divide us, in our 'through' houses, from the back-to-back dwellers opposite, with their outdoor tub closets. In fact it was perceptible between those directly facing us in our back road and those, beyond them, whose windows looked out on Springland Street, despite the fact that, facing them in Springland Street, were also through houses and, indeed, the *fronts* of through houses. To go to the lavatory Freddie Fischer and Arthur Lumb had to come through a passage and walk in front of Mellor or Dyson windows. This might have seemed to reduce the Mellors and Dysons. Not so. The Dysons and the Mellors had the gardens. The feeling was that, by

63

rights, the Fischers and Lumbs ought not to have gone to the lavatory at all, but that they were allowed to do so by gracious permission of the Mellors and Dysons.

I once saw a carthorse fall here. It was pulling a coal cart, and it came in from the top. I was dragged indoors, but I remember the horse on the ground, its long, turning neck, the starting eyeballs. That was a dreadful sight.

There are three steps up from the stone flags of the garden path to that back door, once ours, below the passage now closed. I was not dragged indoors, but (because it was dinner-time) I was not allowed to go round to the scene when, at midday one Saturday, a mill chimney was felled on the far side of the main road. From that back door, over three rows of roof tops, I saw it lean to the left and fall.

The felling of a mill chimney was a public spectacle. Crowds gathered at an advertised time, and photographs taken at the moment of truth were issued as picture postcards. There was prowess in the felling. The main criterion was the smallness of the radius within which the feller got every stone to drop. That, I understood, was a brilliant fall.

There may be pain in every encounter. It was here, too, that I got my first lessons in sociology. I got them from Arthur Lumb and Freddie Fischer. I had taken the scholarship examination. In September, I should be going to the Grange. A month after that, I should be receiving the not-yet-anticipated very bitter lessons in Carlin Beck.

On the first morning of the summer holidays, I saw Freddie Fischer and Arthur Lumb setting off together on an expedition. They carried bottles of Spanish-juice water, sandwiches. They were perhaps off to dam a stream in the bluebell woods beyond Mallalieu Park.

'Where are you baän?' I said.

'Nowhere,' said Freddie Fischer.

Freddie Fischer had a doughy, chinless German face. None of us had ever much liked him. He was simply there, one of us, fairly tough, fairly good at games, a bit bad-tempered and treacherous. We had put up with that.

'Can I come?' I said.

But even petal-skinned Arthur Lumb, tremulous with his strength, his voice high-pitched and gentle, had grown hostile.

'Nay,' he said, 'you're a High School lad now, Harold. Go and laik wi' Leslie Balmforth.'

It was not Brian Solace, Leslie Balmforth and I who despised their proleptic caps and mufflers. It was they who despised our collars and ties.

And yet it was Arthur Lumb I first saw in a hat. That was two years later, twenty-three years ago. We still lived at Carlin Beck, though in the autumn we should return to Hinderholme. I had come to stay with Brian Solace. Walking down Springland Street, I saw Arthur Lumb in long trousers and a hat, wheeling a pram, a young woman by his side. He did not appear to see me, and I made no move to attract his attention.

Brian Solace said it had been a bun-do. That is the local expression for a shot-gun marriage. Arthur Lumb was fifteen, his wife eighteen.

I have not seen Arthur Lumb since. I saw Freddie Fischer in a pub twelve years later, on my last visit to

Hinderholme before the war. I recognised him. He did not recognise me. I re-introduced myself and asked him to have a drink. He refused and turned his back on me.

I am not dishonoured. I have done my best. A world ended. A world began. Humanity was diminished. Literature began. I can even think of the way down to Waterside Lane and the way I must now take as my Swann's way and my Guermantes way in childhood.

To the bottom, then left, then right in the main road. Left, opposite the Fullers' Arms, by the painters' and decorators' shop Mr Solace and his brother shared, down granite-slithering Birklands, over the boisterous Hinder, past further saw-mills, up Holt Hill, under a further railway bridge, past the back entrance to Grange Park, left, right, left, into Holt End. There, inappropriately, will be Uncle Arthur Quarmby. I hope that he at least knows how to make a pot of tea. I could do with a cup of tea.

Down to Waterside Lane was the walk my father and I took on alternate Sunday mornings. This was the way my mother and I went on Saturday afternoons, unless it was raining or she wanted to buy boiled sweets at Dobson's in the covered market. Then we'd go up to Holt End by tram, by two trams, one into town, one up Kirkgate and past the main entrance to Grange Park. Sometimes, my father came up after tea and walked home with us. The Shop closed at four on Saturdays.

A NICE CHAP, MY BROTHER-IN-LAW, GEORGE BINNS. BIG, easy-going, interested in cricket. Kind to Marjorie, friendly in his manner towards my mother. Not much conversation, but we spent a pleasant, relaxed half-hour together at the Woolpack. My mother has found us black ties for to-morrow. Mine is here beside the letters and photographs.

Mother was the last to go to bed. I kept her up, asking questions. Interesting about A'ntie Beulah. Plenty of working-class drama in the family. I suppose we were lower-middle-class. My father worked in a collar and tie. But he was the first man on either side of the family to do so.

Grandad Sykes was a jobbing gardener. Grandma Sykes, *née* Garside, was in service. I remember two of Grandad Sykes's sisters, great-aunts, but only one of them, A'ntie Ruth, lived till I was grown up. She'd married a miner and lived at Thongskirk, a guardswoman, six feet tall, thin, with big feet and a cast in her eye, like Grandad Sykes.

No early photographs of him. One later with a billiard cue, champion of Hinderholme and district. I used to have the gold medal which proved it. One, in solar topee, shorts and puttees, standing at ease with a rifle outside a tent. Heavy, dark moustache. Short, bristly hair.

This is Grandma Sykes. She could sit on her hair. It was fair, like A'ntie Jean's. A'ntie Ada's was fair, but not light gold. Uncle Harry and my mother, Ethel, the eldest, had dark hair.

Our front garden in Radcliffe Road was small. At Holt End, there is only a patch of sooty grass and a grating which admits light and air to the cellar. The stove stands at the head of the cellar steps. The sink is in the living room. Its pair of doors are grained now.

They used to be painted green and always stood open. The piano was in the same room. The house in Waterside Lane was a back-to-back house, but at Waterside Lane there was no smell of poverty. At Holt End there was.

There isn't now. Only the smell of Arthur's Woodbines and a whiff of boiling fat from the chip-shop at the corner. The smell of poverty was the smell of verdigris. It came from the sink, with its brass taps and copper pipes. It came from Uncle Harry's collection of regimental badges. It came from a penny clutched in my hot palm.

There had been some overcrowding, but by the summer of 1917 the congestion had been relieved. Once Uncle Harry went back to the Front, there were only four people to sleep in the two small bedrooms upstairs, and one of those was only four years old. On Saturday afternoons, Grandma Sykes was the only one you could be sure of finding in. A'ntie Ada would be out, with or without Cousin Roy, who was too young for me to play with. A'ntie Jean might be lying down upstairs.

Grandma Sykes sat in a wooden chair like those in the billiard room at the Holt End Conservative Club. A stick leaned against her knee. There was a red shawl about her shoulders. She looked at the hands in her lap, the fingers twisted like roots in a dry soil and brown as if stained with walnut juice. Even after her marriage to Albert Sykes, she had taken in washing or gone out to help with the wash in big houses. As long ago as I can remember, she was almost wholly immobile with arthritis and could only read with the help of a magnifying glass.

I knew that Uncle Harry was in the Northumberland Fusiliers. I seem to remember that he wore a Glengarry bonnet with green facings. I don't know if that is possible, and my mother doesn't remember. From this roneoed War Office letter, it seems that he was in the 1/5 (Territorial) Battalion, that his regimental number was 40595 and that he had enlisted at Halifax. He was a big man, my mother says, and very lively. He, too, had been a gardener.

He had been home twice that year, once on ordinary leave and once with a head wound. Between the two visits, his father had also enlisted, though over-age. Grandad Sykes had been posted off to join Allenby's Egypt Expeditionary Force.

My mother says Harry went back wilfully, his wound unhealed. This letter states that 40595, Pte. Sykes, H., was last seen on October 26th, as were a hundred and sixty-three other men of his battalion, including a dozen or so from Hinderholme. At first he was posted Missing, then Presumed Killed. All those men went squelching woefully off, with bayonets fixed, in the direction of a derelict village called Passchendaele, which a few days later the Canadians entered unopposed. That morning, I dare say Private Sykes had a headache.

The letter graphically describes the confusion. I remember it coming. Or, rather, I remember my mother reading the letter aloud to Grandma Sykes, who had mislaid her magnifying glass. That was on a Saturday afternoon, no doubt in November. I listened, comprehending but strangely unimplicated.

Grandma Sykes managed to get one rheumaticky

hand and one failing eye to meet. She slowly rubbed them together.

'Ay, well,' she said.

Grandad Sykes had been luckier in his moment. On the day of his son's death, he lay opposite Gaza, which a few days later fell, 21st Corps artillery having been joined by the guns of French and British warships from the sea. His letters to my mother (written in pencil and now mouldering in their official green envelopes) once also contained exotic flowers and sketches one of his companions had done of him in their tent. These have gone.

I remember my mother reading this long letter aloud to visitors. It goes:

The first hundred and fifty miles were very uninteresting. Sand, sand everywhere and a burning sun overhead. The only shelter that I got was by rigging up my ground sheet to some long poles stuck up in the truck and lying underneath, with my water-bottle close at hand, for this is your best friend in the desert.

The first place of note was Gaza, where Samson pulled down the pillars, but it looks now as if a lot of strong men had been there, for it is in ruins. This is the place where the Allies were held up so long. I believe that we were hammering at it for over twelve months. The town was well-protected by hills. In fact it had the appearance of being in the centre of a ring of hills, horse-shoe shape, and we had to approach it from the front or open side. It cost us very dearly.

The train stopped five hours, and you bet that I had a good hunt round the place, for you must know that now the country had changed from the desert to cultivation, and I found several very interesting plants and insects. Then next morning you could see miles of orange-groves and orchards, and I bought some lovely oranges, four for twopence-halfpenny.

It further appears from this letter that Uncle Jim, Ruth Sykes's husband, was at the time near Gaza but that Grandad Sykes could not get to see him. It seems that Jim Brierley was in fact batman to a *Times* correspondent in that area.

The next place-name is one I cannot read.

This is where we had to trans-ship all our goods from the broad-gauge railway to the narrow-gauge railway of the Turks. This took thirty hours. I had a great time hunting butterflies and gathering wild flowers amongst them the blue pimpernel (*Anagalis cerulium*).

He must previously have sent a pressed specimen of this, for I am reported as having asked about it.

The Enab ridge and the hill of En Sabi Samweil were taken in fog, and the 75th Division spent weeks in those cold, damp passes. German aeroplanes bombed a train in which Grandad Sykes was riding. Jaffa fell in November. By Christmas, Grandad Sykes was in Jerusalem.

After my breakfast I went into the town to get my name put down for a party from the Y.M.C.A. to visit the Ancient City. No soldier is allowed inside those walls unless he is with one of these parties, which consist of fourteen and a Y.M.C.A. conductor. There are two parties march out morning and afternoon, one party inside the walls and one party outside. I was too late for the morning visit, owing to a little mistake that I made, for I went into the town without belt and very nearly got run in, so had to turn back and get properly dressed. I spent the rest of the morning looking around the town. Of course, the *town* and the City are two different places. The City is the ancient place inside the walls. What I call the town is outside.

I made no mistake about dress in the afternoon and started off about two o'clock. Our conductor knew his business, and I think he knew the life of Christ off by heart. The first place he took us to was the Temple of Omar or the Temple of the Rock. This was the most beautiful place that ever I had the pleasure to see. The decorations, gold and silver, windows, lamps, carpets, pictures, marble pillars, were magnificent past my power to describe. I forgot to tell you that, before entering this temple of Solomon, we had to take off our boots or put on slippers. Here again I delayed the party, for the little children who brought us our slippers could not find any large enough to go on top of my boots. But they were equal to the occasion, for they ripped the slippers open and made them fit. We paid half a *piastre*, one and a quarter for the loan of the slippers.

Inside the mosque there is a very large rock covering the centre of the floor. I think he said it was sixty feet long and twenty feet wide. Around this rock are beautiful carved rails, then around the rails marvellous carpets perhaps fourteen feet wide, then marble pillars holding up a gallery and overhead, at a great height, a beautiful dome all decorated in gold and great windows consisting of millions of pieces of coloured glass, like mosaic-work.

We then went down into places under the rock, just as fine, only they were lighted by artificial light. Down here the conductor showed us where Solomon, Abraham and David used to pray.

After coming out of this temple, we visited the Temple of Justice. This was a place all open, only having a great dome over, from which hung a long chain to within about ten feet of the floor. Under this chain the prisoner had to stand and give his evidence. If he was telling the truth, nothing happened, but if he was lying the chain was supposed to swing slightly. I am afraid that, if some of the war correspondents had stood under, the chain would have done some swinging.

Next we saw the exact spot where Christ was brought out to show the multitude, and then we saw the place where He was crucified. Here we saw a bust of Mary, the mother of Christ, and you talk about jewels. On her neck were necklaces, on her fingers were rings, and on her chest were honours brought by people out of their love for her Son. Altogether there was supposed to be £160,000 worth of valuables on her.

Then we went from one place to another, and all were beautiful.

After that, Grandad Sykes left Jerusalem. On his last visit into the town, he looked for souvenirs, but about the only things on sale were mother-of-pearl beads and olive-wood toys. He bought two books of pressed flowers and views, with olive-wood covers, one each for Cousin Roy and me. I still have mine. The views are, as Grandad Sykes says, 'very common', but then, as he also says, he just got them for the sake of the place. This letter promises to send them on later.

I set off to go to Bethlehem, the place where Christ was born, but it was so hot and the roads so dusty that I turned back. The place is very hilly, and the roads are inches deep in white dust. Motor-lorries are flying in every direction.

The track lay down a valley between two mountains, and the line occasionally crossed the valley on high bridges, all new, the old ones having been blown down by the Turks. We could see the broken masses of twisted ironwork lying underneath.

All up the hill-side you could see the natives busy cultivating the ground, clearing the stones and building a sort of dry wall. A few yards of level ground, then another wall and another level patch, like steps. These level patches were all planted with various kinds of vegetables and fruits, and down the walls you could see vine-trees trailing. I saw a native ploughing with an ox and a donkey, another with a camel, and in both cases the plough was a large crooked branch. In one part of the line, where the hill was all rocks, thousands of Indians were at work drilling holes and blasting to make the line wider, ready for the English broad gauge.

A very common plant growing wild was the hollyhock, and locust trees were very common. I was very pleased when we arrived at the bottom. It took us five days to reach camp. Then I received the news of Roy's death, which quite put a damper on everything. . . .

The last page is missing. My mother destroyed it. I used to borrow the letter from her to read, and it contained things she didn't want me to know about.

'About Cousin Roy?'

'Yes.'

'Who *was* his father?'

As a child, I was given to understand that Cousin Roy was A'ntie Ada's little boy and also that he was Grandad Sykes's little boy. This seemed an unusual arrangement. I knew of no other case in which a child's father was also its grandfather. However, I did not at that time pursue the matter further.

'We never discovered. An'tie Ada was very obstinate.'

The year before war broke out, three years after my mother had married and left home, Grandma Sykes formed the impression that Ada was pregnant, but found her big, quick-tempered youngest daughter not at all easy to talk to and so, on a Saturday afternoon, when I was two, asked my mother, her married daughter to broach the subject.

A'ntie Ada denied that there was any question of a baby.

'You'll be sorry for what you've said, Ethel,' was her indignant, faintly menacing comment.

It also fell to my mother to go round to the Conservative Club, meet Grandad Sykes and explain matters to him away from the house. Grandad Sykes was a violent man in drink. He had been known to strike his wife. His first reaction might have been a blow. He might have felled A'ntie Ada.

The letter had contained dark speculations on Cousin Roy's parentage, threats against the child's father if he were discovered. For all that ever transpired was that the man had been 'a footballer'. A'ntie Ada never divulged his name, nor did she ever reveal whether the game he played was F.A. or Rugby League football. Perhaps she had never enquired, or perhaps she did not know the difference. Grandad Sykes himself followed the Rugby League game at Nether End.

When Cousin Roy was born, Grandad Sykes became very fond of the child. Then, in the last year of the war, while Grandad Sykes was in Egypt, Cousin Roy, aged five, became suddenly ill, would not eat, lost all interest in his toys.

At times, he cried. At times, he pressed his fingers to his head. He could not go to the lavatory. He was sick. At one moment, he seemed to be having a fit. Then he held his head to one side like an idiot. He tossed and turned all night and towards morning began to scream in a peculiar manner. He was very hot.

He became quieter. The pain seemed to have gone. At the same time, Cousin Roy's eyes looked funny. One of his eyelids drooped. He could not see properly. He squinted. He could not tell, and did not care, who was standing by his bed.

Then it started again. The doctor said it was meningitis and that there was nothing he could do. At one moment unable to move, at another convulsed, Cousin Roy screamed all night again and died.

My mother had spent some nights by his bedside, while A'ntie Ada slept, but a telegram came to Radcliffe Road in the end. Those were the only uses we knew for telegrams, to announce death and to say that one had arrived safely wherever it might be. My mother took to clutching the backs of chairs whenever a telegraph boy passed the house. The Angel of Death was keeping his eye on us.

Earlier in the year, A'ntie Jean had died. She died of TB. I was taken to see her laid out, as fair a corse as we could expect to have in the family. I remember her in pre-Raphaelite terms, the hair braided, the stem of a lily between the folded hands. The picture cannot in actual fact have been quite like that, but certainly the chilly presence of death did not at a first view appear to me to be unbeautiful.

THAT WAS A VERY STRANGE THING TO HEAR ABOUT A'ntie Beulah. In appearance, she was respectable lower-middle-class spinsterhood incarnate. In manner, she was frail and tremulous. Upon her flat bosom she wore a cameo brooch, to which, by a thin gold chain, her *pince-nez* were attached. Like Ma Wrigley, the Infants' headmistress, her long frock was of dark-blue bombasine. Her bony temples were insufficiently masked by hair. A black velvet band encircled her goitrous throat. The cameo brooch sat on a kind of lace bib. A'ntie Beulah was ten years my father's senior. At fifty, the backs of her thin hands were covered with the brown mottle of decrepitude.

And it turns out that she, too, had experienced love or something of the kind. Even my mother had not heard of this until A'ntie Beulah died in this house during the recent war. Then my father told her. Beulah had once borne an illegitimate child. Unlike Cousin Roy, it had died at a few days old, though it had lived long enough to cause some awkwardness in the small village out in the country beyond Cowl Hill.

It was the shame attached to this episode which had finally decided Grandad Atha to move into Hinder-holme and work for the Co-op. But in fact A'ntie Beulah's love-life was not yet over, at fifty.

When Grandad Atha died, A'ntie Beulah took in to live with her at the house in Waterside Lane a Miss Toothill, cashier at the Co-op restaurant and thus her immediate second-in-command there. One Sunday morning, in the summer of 1922, when my father and I walked down by way of Hoyland Brig to Waterside Lane, Miss Toothill was out.

In her accustomed place on the couch sat a man with a dark, waxed moustache (my father's by then was certainly shorter and unwaxed). He was older than my father. He wore a gold watch-chain across a splendid paunch, and his white neck bulged opulently over his collar. He was smoking a cigar with the band on. His name was Mr Haigh, and A'ntie Beulah addressed him as Nathan.

Over the piano at A'ntie Beulah's stood the framed sepia photograph of Grandad Atha holding the head of a horse on which my father sat, aged ten. On the sideboard, beneath a glass dome, stood my father's most elaborate creation, a work of his later youth. It was a clock built into a fretwork castle. There were eighty-four little fretwork men on the battlements.

I counted them while Mr Haigh, in a measured speech at once orotund and marked by dialectal peculiarities unfamiliar to me, communicated the nature of his position in life to the male head of his intended's family. When my father and I left, A'ntie Beulah gave me the usual twopence. Mr Haigh gave me sixpence and showed me his gold watch. I was instructed to call him Uncle Nathan.

When we had eaten our Yorkshire pudding and my father was thoughtfully cutting up the roll of brisket, my mother said:

'So Beulah's got a young man?'

My father raised his pale-blue eyes and gazed for a moment through the scullery window, then returned to his carving. He transmitted to my mother the various details I might have taken in earlier if I had considered them interesting, that Nathan Haigh was a director of the Hinderholme Co-operative and Industrial Society and sat on the restaurant sub-committee, that he was a widower with two grown-up daughters, that he lived in Bradford Road, that he was a mill-worker but that he had got a bit put by, already owned his house and would presently be retiring. The two daughters lived at home, but one of them had been engaged for some years, and the other was only waiting for a house in order to get married. The idea was that she should take over A'ntie Beulah's house in Waterside

Lane when A'ntie Beulah married Uncle Nathan.

'He'll make her a good husband,' said my father.

My mother began to serve out the kind of potatoes known south of the Trent as roast and north of it as baked.

'Your A'ntie Beulah's courting,' she explained to me, with her brave smile.

I could, I felt, have been expected to gather as much, but I refrained from disrespectful comment.

It further transpired that Uncle Nathan was a big Labour man and that he drank his tea out of a pint pot. This was a matter of some practical importance. He would be coming to tea the following Sunday. My mother argued that there was no essential connection between the two ideas, since Mr Dyson, across the road at the back, voted Labour but drank his tea from a cup, while Grandad Sykes, who voted Conservative, had always used a pint pot when she lived at home.

My father broke up this bit of mild flyting by saying that *I* was a socialist. This notion arose from the fact that, a few weeks before, my father having come up to Holt End to bring us home after his Saturday tea, I had said, as we looked over the Hinder valley from that side, that all the money in the world ought to be put together and then re-shared equally. I now pointed out that this idea would never have occurred to me had I not heard him and my mother express discontentment over some people having too much and some too little money.

The following Sunday, Nathan Haigh and A'ntie Beulah came to tea. We had got Uncle Nathan a beautiful blue-and-white-banded pint mug to drink his tea from, and drink it he did with noises like those of a parched lion at a pool and no nonsense about waiting until it cooled, but pouring into the saucer and appreciative belches. His behaviour throughout was of an uncompromising saga-like coarseness. This, it seemed to my mother, was not setting me a good example, but, in view of the indubitable strength of his character, she rapidly forgave Uncle Nathan his lack of gentility.

His way of speaking belonged to the upper Helm valley, more precisely to Helm-in-Elmet, known as Twice-it. For 'he' and 'she' he used 'oo' and 'shoo' indifferently. That is to say, it was not a matter of 'oo' for 'he' and 'shoo' for 'she', but either for either according to the euphony of the sentence. Ten years later, I should discover that this practice had been given up in most forms of English by Chaucer's time.

The previous winter, I had had a season ticket for the Hilderholme United football ground, Bradford Road. From my seat in the grandstand I had often noticed people sitting at their bedroom windows in houses beyond the far terrace. Uncle Nathan's house was one of these. From his back bedroom windows, you could see the full length of the ground and about two thirds of its breadth, as I discovered when my family went to tea in Bradford Road the following Sunday.

Also there were the two daughters and their young men, whose names were, respectively, Gordon Broadbent and Johnny Lenihan. Gordon Broadbent was a beetle-browed, fiery-complexioned man with dark, wavy hair. He said very little and seemed a bit thickheaded, though it appeared that he and Gertie were friendly with the United players, including the many-times capped international left full-back. The older daughter had massed, wavy hair of a natural Titian-red. She also had dimples. She laughed frequently and was clearly of a dutiful and affectionate nature. She was much too fat. Her white, flaccid cheeks trembled like *blanc-mange* when she moved. Vera, her younger sister, was small, neat and attractively plump.

Gordon Broadbent worked at the same mill as Gertie. Johnny Lenihan worked at the British Dyes. He, too, had wavy hair, but it was fairer. He was short, round-faced, blue-eyed.

When we had got away from the house and were waiting at the tram stop, my mother announced:

'Johnny Lenihan's Irish.'

This puzzled me. Johnny Lenihan's face spoke eloquently of soap and a sharp razor. His hair and clothes were spotless. He was not drunk. He had not shouted, spilt anything on the tablecloth, spat in the fire, thrown his overcoat on the couch, kicked up the mats, trailed in mud or done anything Irish, so far as I could see. In fact, of the two, I should have said that Johnny Lenihan was less Irish than Gordon Broadbent. It appeared, however, that my mother was using the term in a specialised, geographical sense.

My father said that Johnny Lenihan seemed a very agreeable young man.

'Is he a Roman Catholic?' said my mother.

'I don't know, I'm sure, lass,' said my father. 'I expect so.'

'Does he live in Wellgate?' said my mother.

'No.'

'Well, that's something.'

Johnny Lenihan married Vera Haigh and went to live in Waterside Lane. At the same time, A'ntie Beulah was married and went to live in Bradford Road, no longer manageress of the Co-op restaurant in town.

The Boxing Day party that year was at Uncle Nathan's. Whisky, rum and brandy were poured in the tea. Balloons popped on the holly, in the fireplace or on the glowing tips of cigars. Paper caps split with the heat. I accompanied the singing, from *The Scottish Students' Song Book*, of 'Jingle Bells', 'Solomon Levi', 'Clementine', 'Riding down from Bangor'. A bit tipsy and a fierier red than ever, the uncommunicative Gordon Broadbent smoothed out his corrugated brow, allowed his long jaw to droop and grinned amiably at the company. The many-times-capped international full-back looked in for an hour with one of his teammates. With fascinated horror, I saw the two huge-shouldered, bulging-thighed heroes drinking beer, which I had supposed fatal to footballers and athletes. The ladies and I were teetotallers. We stuck to port.

In due course, Johnny and Vera Lenihan had a little girl, whose soul they duly sold to the priest at St. Patrick's. There was some hint of drama in that, but at the time none at all in Gordon Broadbent, though Gertie was still at home and Gordon's continued failure to propose a date for their marriage gave rise to discontentment.

I suppose that to-morrow we shall drive out of Hinderholme by way of Bradford Road. First, my father's body in a hearse piled high with gladioli. Then the one car in which sit my mother, my sister, George Binns and myself, with the soft-voiced cobbler from

Molethorpe and Arthur Quarmby with his squashed Punchinello face and stiff, waving grey hair, a man despised by my mother.

We shall pass first the 'bus stop, then, to the right, the road in which the turnstiles to the United ground stand unturning, then the house in which A'ntie Beulah, Uncle Nathan and Gertie once lived and to which Gertie returned after so short an absence twenty-one years ago. Then, off to the left, the house Gordon Broadbent had not long rented. I suppose that one can see it from the main road. I am not sure that I should recognise it. I saw it only once. I am not altogether sure I shall want to look.

The fever hospital also lies further out in that direction, east-north-east. I went there by ambulance after dark on a Saturday in January, 1923. I was feverish and I had a very sore throat. Dr Holroyd said it was scarlet fever. Four weeks later, I went back home in a taxi by daylight.

Of course, on Sunday afternoons, once I was out of bed, my parents had been allowed to smile and gesticulate at me through a window. When they had gone, a nurse would bring in the grapes, cake and comics they had left. As the taxi turned up Radcliffe Road, I saw that the door of our house stood open and that Marjorie was there on the doorstep, a child of two and a half, wearing small brown laced boots, her hair bobbed with a fringe. I thought how quickly she had grown. My mother and father joined her, and they stood in a welcoming group by the newly budded Dorothy Perkins climber which so admiredly surrounded our front window. As the taxi drew up, I thought what nice faces all three had. I had not previously thought of Marjorie as having a face at all, and I had always considered Brian Solace's mother better-looking than mine. They both had the same name, Ethel.

IT WAS TWO AND A HALF YEARS BEFORE THAT, IN MID-October, I had been awakened towards midnight by my father. He had wrapped a blanket round me and carried me next door but one to sleep with Brian Solace.

I asked:

'Can we talk?'

My father said no, we must go to sleep. I had my breakfast at Mrs Solace's, then called in at home on the way to school. Overhead, I could hear my mother still moaning. I did not ask why, though, so far as I knew, babies were simply brought by Dr Holroyd. Either I was very unobservant or Kenneth Fainwright is right about repression, for I had paid no attention either to my mother's big belly or to her unwonted lassitude. I was nine.

For three weeks thereafter, a grey-haired woman lived in the house. That was the first, and would be the only, time my parents had employed anything in the nature of a servant. The Sunday after her departure, my sister was christened at the Wesleyans in the afternoon after Sunday School. I sat in the gallery and watched my parents come out of the vestry and stand by the altar-rail, Marjorie carefully folded in a white shawl in my mother's arms. My parents comported themselves to my satisfaction, and the baby did not cry. All the same, I did not like having the family on show.

After the ceremony, one of the young men who marked star-cards told me how babies were born. Next day, I told Brian Solace. At dinner-time on Wednesday, my father called me upstairs. Evidently, Brian had told his mother what I had said, and Mrs Solace had told my mother, who had passed on the problem as one for my father to deal with.

I expected punishment, the preliminaries to which generally took this formal course. That the occasion for punishment had arisen would normally be decided by my mother, who then handed me over to my father like a heretic to the secular arm. It was one of their frequently enunciated principles that a child should never be struck in anger. I doubt whether they always recognised anger when they felt it, but in practice not a great deal of striking was done. On the whole, I would say that my father was temperamentally less disposed to administer punishment than my mother to recommend it.

It turned out on this occasion that my father only wanted to know if I had got the facts of life right. I was made to repeat what the star-card-marker at Sunday school had told me. As this account seemed reasonably accurate, nothing was added to it by my father. I found the occasion puzzling. I had supposed that he wanted to estimate the gravity of my offence in telling Brian Solace, who was younger than me by almost a year.

I was nine years old. That is hardly the end of childhood, though perhaps its closer, nestling stages are over. In several ways, the birth of a sister marked a phase in mine.

To the child herself, my feelings were in general friendly. The crying at night sometimes upset my parents, but I was disturbed only by their agitation. I was not often required to wheel a perambulator about the streets of Linfootlock. There was sometimes a queue of little girls at the door wanting to know if they could take the baby out. On one occasion when I was away from school and the duty did fall to me, it was reported by a neighbour to my mother that my sister was crying and that I had threatened to kill her if she didn't stop at once. On the other hand, somewhat later, when bathing and powdering operations had somehow devolved upon my father, and he began slapping her bottom because she would not keep still, I flew at him, outraged, and seized his arm.

It was instructive to contemplate the principal feminine *differentia* at more leisure than I had once enjoyed with Sylvia Jagger. However genuine or otherwise my information might be about how babies were born, there was clearly a *prima facie* plausibility about the method by which they were supposed to be made.

In Radcliffe Road and Springland Street, in the Wreck and at school and Sunday school, the subject became one of absorbing interest, any interest of the same order having previously centred upon the excretory functions. The authoritative source of information on the subject was understood to be *Aristotle's Works.* I do not recall ever seeing a copy of this treatise at the time, nor do I remember which of the Radcliffe Road and Springland Street gang had a copy at home.

We had none. We had a small medical dictionary. We had two other dictionaries, a Nuttall's and one in black morocco with coloured pictures. They, I suppose, are still in the music cabinet, made by my father, downstairs in the shadowy room which contains his coffin and him and the gladioli in buckets. We had the *Harmsworth's Universal Encyclopaedia*, bought in fortnightly instalments, bound up in red just before I went to the fever hospital. There it stands in the glass-fronted cupboard, alongside the *Cassell's Illustrated History of England* in eight volumes bought before I can remember.

Before I can remember, the only other books in the house would be Nuttall's and the medical dictionary, a Bible and four Sunday-school prizes of my mother's. Two of these were stories of orphans in Victorian London. The other two were missionary accounts of Japan and China. All these no doubt are still in the music cabinet downstairs. When my father has gone from that room, I shall look.

The glass-fronted cupboard is deep, and the books there stand in two rows, one in front of the other. Some of them are my sister's, but most are still mine or were mine or first known by me. *The Queen's Gift Book*. A *Holiday Annual*, 1921, a *Chums Annual*, 1922. The Ballantynes, *The Dog Crusoe*, *The Coral Island*, *Erling the Bold*, *The World of Ice*, *Ungava*. Two by G. Manville Fenn, the one set in Brazil, which I re-read almost as often as *The Dog Crusoe*, and the one in Australia, which I cared for less. The little key is loose, and the doors wobble, squeaking. I mustn't wake anybody.

This small, flexible Bible was bought for me when I read the lesson at the Anniversary. It was a good deal later when I took to reading it for pleasure. The pictures instance some particular text, but they also bear titles of a general and timeless application. These are money-changers in a street of modern Jerusalem. There are hides being wrung and copper beaten, an Egyptian peasant watering the soil 'with his foot', statutes and laws on the doorpost of a Jew's house, Jews at the wailing wall, a woman gathering clusters from 'the vine with the tender grapes', peasants winnowing, fishermen mending nets.

Such figures had passed before the eyes of Grandad Sykes and of Uncle Jim Brierley at Thongskirk. The views and pressed flowers and mother-of-pearl beads and Turkish coins added further to their reality for me. First read aloud with pride to visitors by my mother, Grandad Sykes's letters had taught me that a person one knew, a member of one's own family, could write in such a way as to give the sort of pleasure that was to be got from books. In a world quite unfamiliar with the persons of writers, this was a revelation. I might easily write a book myself.

One like this, for instance. *The Return of Tarzan*. I remember that as beginning, ' "*Magnifique!*" said the Countess . . .' Not quite. It begins:

'*Magnifique!*' ejaculated the Countess de Coude, beneath her breath.

'Eh,' questioned the count, turning towards his young wife. 'What is it that is magnificent?' and the count bent his eyes in various directions in quest of the object of her admiration.

If he had got them straightened out before going below to play cards, the figure on whom the Count de Coude's eyes would have alighted would, of course, have been none other than John Clayton, Lord Greystoke, 'with a seat in the House of Lords', Tarzan himself, taking the air on a transatlantic liner. Later, the Count ('the best marksman in France') was to fight a duel with Tarzan. Inevitably, the Countess's name was Olga.

Four of them here. *Tarzan of the Apes* itself. *The Return. The Beasts of Tarzan, Jungle Tales of Tarzan, Tarzan and the Jewels of Opar*. Frenchmen always behave with fabulous courage and possess a highly developed sense of fair play. That is a notion I picked up from these books. Some black tribes are good, some bad. Arabs and Belgians are vicious slave-traders. Among Russians, you meet conspiracy and assassination Largely, I find that all these notions have stuck. Of course, I liked the tune of the *Marseillaise*. Whenever I heard it, shivers ran up and down my spine. Also, I'd won sixpence in a bet with Frank Mellor when Georges Carpentier beat Joe Beckett.

Enough to make a lifelong Francophile. Seven or eight weeks ago, Alain Thomas took me into Carpentier's smart bar in one of the little streets which connect the great avenues of Paris just before they converge on the Arc de Triomphe. There he was, suave among his rich *clientèle*. A bit of a clip-joint, I thought it. I'd seen French clip-joints before. They don't disturb what I felt at the age of eleven.

I first saw *Tarzan of the Apes* as a film, featuring, as they said then (not starring), Elmo Lincoln. That was at a cinema in town, not at the Ellen Brig bughouse where, on Thursday evenings, Leslie Balmforth, Brian Solace, Freddie Fischer, Arthur Lumb and a quorum of other Radcliffe Roaders and Springland Streeters, having paid threepence, sat in the front three rows, cheering Tom Mix or Buck Jones, falling off our seats with noisy laughter as the custard pies flew between Ben Turpin or Buster Keaton or Fatty Arbuckle and their foes, rigid with apprehension as a train roared towards Pearl White or Ruth Roland bound across the track or as Harold Lloyd raced up and down sky-scrapers, betweenwhiles shouting at the members of alien gangs or fighting with our neighbours until the chucker-out came and quelled us.

Then I read the books. Put them in their places. Back to bed. The stabbing, the breaking of necks, the miscellaneous blood and cruelty were no doubt part of the attraction. In the concrete playground at Linfootlock Elementary School, we exerted the full Nelson on each other's necks. Nobody's spinal cord actually snapped. We placed one foot upon the prostrate bodies of our foes, drummed upon our chests and bayed out what we imagined the victory cry of the great anthropoids to be like. The film, being silent, didn't help us there.

But that was not all. In *Jungle Tales*, there were Mowgliesque speculations on God and the universe. The ape-child sat in any available tree on a sunny day and speculated on God and the universe. In *The Return of Tarzan*, there was adumbrated a whole world of cosmopolitan sophistication. Since one had not yet read *She* by Rider Haggard, one's first glimpse of woman as the destructive white goddess was in *Tarzan and the Jewels of Opar*.

Above all, there was swinging through the trees.

The levitation phantasies are among mankind's happiest. *Tarzan* combined them with the powerful images of hunting. I lay in bed then, as I do now, between flannelette sheets. Sometimes I had the momentary fear that I should awake to find myself in the street, clad in only, not a loin-cloth, but my shirt. At other times, the mind's ear created the sounds of a jungle night. From branch to branch, one sped through the tree-tops with tireless arms into a dreamless sleep.

III

MY FATHER WAS STAYING WITH SOME PEOPLE CALLED Cowan in a small town called Carlin Beck in that part of the North Riding known as Cleveland. It was fifty or sixty miles away to the north-east. My father had changed his job. He was managing the drapery and hardware of a small independent co-operative society. He liked Carlin Beck. He wanted us to go and live there.

That August, there were no holidays at Blackpool, Morecambe or Scarborough. Instead, my mother and I and Marjorie, not yet three, also went and stayed with the Cowans in Carlin Beck for ten days.

On a hot afternoon, my father and I walked together along the sunny side of the high street. In Carlin Beck, all but a few old houses were made of brick, and the causeways were concrete. The church was pale-grey stone. By it, the road bore left in a grand sweep. The boys' entrance to the Grammar School lay that way, but my father and I walked along a narrow, flagged path by the churchyard wall. The school and the school-house were also pale-grey stone. They were very old and looked historical. The schoolhouse door was set in a low arch, rather ecclesiastical in form. It was answered by a boy a year or so older than myself, a thin boy with bony temples and large brown eyes.

'Oh, you want the Boss,' he said, and he went off into the garden which lay beyond the arch.

From behind a row of sweet peas appeared a heavily built, bald-headed man. He was in his shirt-sleeves, but wore a dog collar, a square of black silk hanging from it at the front. He also wore a small, closely trimmed moustache, reddish in colour but fairer than my father's. 'Boy' Allendale showed us into his father's study, where there were book-shelves, leather armchairs, photographs of cricket and Rugby teams and groups of Army officers, college shields, a desk with a swivel chair. Presently, Mr Allendale reappeared, wearing the kind of black alpaca jacket my father sometimes wore at the Shop.

The only Anglican parson I had previously been much aware of was the one in Linfootlock. Despite his albinism (indeed, to some extent because of it), he looked every inch a parson, a stage parson, a Gilbert and Sullivan parson. One could imagine him pinkly made up as the lovesick Dr Daly in *The Sorcerer* (a part I seven years later played at the Wesleyans). He was very short, with black trilby hat, umbrella, stiff-kneed, teetering gait. The few words I ever heard him speak were thin, prim and, as it happened, indignant.

The Rev. G. L. M. Allendale, M.A., was not at all like that. If there was any stage figure he resembled, it was rather that of a Major in the Army. His was the first convincingly upper-middle-class, southern-English voice I had heard off the stage. There was even something a bit raffish about his choice of terms. For instance to put me at my ease, he addressed me as 'old man'. I liked him well enough. He did not speak to my father condescendingly, though his eyes, identically pale-blue with my father's (these serious, his quizzical), had a man-of-the-world knowingness about them and pouches of skin underneath. My father sat on the edge of one of the leather armchairs, the trousers of his navy-blue, faintly shiny suit pulled up too high, so that they showed the brown-and-green mixture of home-knitted socks above his boots, a billycock hat on his knees, between his nicely made hands. Mr Allendale sat at his desk, turning the chair towards us.

Outside the window trailed a branch of ivy, a blue-tit swinging on it. The sun burned in the room. In the distance, the ridge of Long Topping seemed dented by the heat. I was not unhappy, but I hoped that what was here being transacted might somehow never come to pass.

I had left the board school. In a few weeks' time, I was due to start at the Grange. The North Riding education authorities at Northallerton had agreed, however, that once my father had found a house in Carlin Beck my scholarship could be transferred from Hinderholme, if the headmaster at Carlin Beck found me a place. Carlin Beck Grammar School was not at all like the Grange, in that parents normally paid for their sons to be at it. It was a small school. There were only about a hundred and thirty boys, most of whom came from outside Carlin Beck, though latterly there were no boarders, so that they travelled up daily by train or lodged in the town.

The blue-tit had just flown away. The ivy-branch waved up and down.

'. . . If there isn't a place, we'll make one,' said Mr Allendale, and he turned to me.

'What kind of football do you play, Atha?' he said.

'Well, both,' said I, 'Sir.'

I was aware that in the south of England there existed a fifteen-a-side game also known as Rugby, but I did not suppose that it could enter into calculations made nearly sixty miles north of Hinderholme.

'Afraid we're a soccer school here, old man,' said the Boss. 'Still, there's always the O.T.C. We're attached to the Green Howards. I dare say you'll enjoy a bit of drill and musketry.'

He glanced sideways at my father, as though wishing to detect any sign of dissent. None was made.

There came a knock at the door.

'Hello?' said the Boss.

'*Mater* says will you come.'

'You'd better show yourself, old man.'

'Boy' Allendale came in, gazelle-like and rather charming, very serious. Mr Allendale explained that 'Boy' would be at this school for another year, then go on to Winchester, Eton or wherever it was.

'This,' he said, 'is Atha. He'll be in the Second. And, of course, this is *Mr* Atha.'

My father said:

'Hello, young man.'

'Boy' said:

'How do you do, sir? Hello, Atha. Hope you'll like it here.'

Then he repeated his message.

'Yes, coming,' said the Boss, 'Well, Mr Atha, I shall see your son here again when you've found a house. I'm sure he'll fit in very nicely.'

He stood up. My father stood up, the turn-up of one trousers leg catching on the top of his boot, descending to its place as he moved again.

'Eh, old man?' said the Boss to me.

My father and he shook hands. 'Boy' Allendale let us out into the archway. My father and I turned our backs on a vague prospect of outbuildings and playing-fields and regained the flagged path by the churchyard wall. To the left on flat ground stood the Priory ruins, the already perceptibly westering sun upon them.

'Well,' said my father, as we turned right and marched off towards church and high street, 'he seems a very nice man, does Mr Allendale.'

I agreed. That did not make me want to leave Hinderholme and live here, though.

'I suppose it'll be all right,' said my father, 'you playing at soldiers. I don't expect they waste a lot of time on it. I must see if I can't get them to let me stock caps and school-ties at the Shop.'

The Carlin Beck cap was black, with a green St. Oswald in a yellow niche. The stripes of the knitted tie were yellow and green. A draper called Mayhew on the south side of the high street stocked both caps and ties exclusively. The tie at the Grange was red-and-white, the cap red with a white shield containing three sheep's heads.

The Cowans were satirical about Mr Allendale. They understood that there was much to be said in his favour. He captained the town's second team at cricket, which was democratic of him, and he was good at Latin. They remembered him mainly, however, as a recruiting officer during the war. At this, they said, he was very keen. As to the fact that he was on visiting terms with Lord Cleveland, the Cowans did not think much of that. Mr Cowan recalled, at election time, helping, in the Liberal interest, to overturn Lord Cleveland's carriage with Lord and Lady Cleveland in it.

Already in 1923, there was acute poverty in Carlin Beck. In that small country town I saw what I had never seen in Hinderholme, numerous children going about barefoot. There was very little work at the iron-stone mines. Mr Cowan and his married son George hardly ever had work. Luckily, the Cowans owned their house, and Mr Cowan grew a fair amount of food in his allotment, while their daughter, Jenny, had married a man called Jack Greenlees, who worked as a clerk at a steel works in Grangetown or somewhere about the mouth of the Tees.

He played the piano. Jenny sang. He was very dark. Jenny was very fair. He was rather short, she a Valkyrie. She and her mother both had heads of marvellous, truly flaxen hair. At sixty, Mrs Cowan's hair was hardly touched with grey at all, and, as she said, she had never lost a tooth. This last boast was accompanied by the statement that neither had she ever cleaned her teeth. This showed. Moreover, she wore steel-rimmed spectacles, and some of her facial expressions were very foolish. Yet here, certainly, was a magnificent and, one supposes, radically Scandinavian physical strain. Though perhaps too big-limbed for a perfect drawing-room elegance, both mother and daughter might have

98

been great beauties. With his dark skin, his pointed, inquisitive nose and protruding, brown, intelligent, melancholy eyes, Jack Greenlees looked a bit foreign.

The father, Tom Cowan, had also never lost a tooth or cleaned one. He, too, was tall. He was moderately dark, with much the same stiff fringe and heavy moustache as Grandad Sykes. He walked in a more stately manner than Grandad Sykes, having somewhat of a paunch to support. He smoked a pipe, cutting up his tobacco with a pen-knife in the palm of his hand. Mrs Cowan bought him two ounces of this solid plug tobacco every Saturday morning. At the same time, she gave him five shillings pocket money, he having handed over to her the previous evening, whatever dole and/or wages he had. This was to us a curiously matriarchal arrangement.

I liked the Cowans, especially Mr Cowan. I admired Jenny's looks, the nose straight as though drawn with a ruler, the high yet smoothly rounded cheek-bones tilting her grey eyes and attractively pulling up the corners of her mouth into a smile. I was amused by Jack Greenlees's patter songs.

Jenny Greenlees, *née* Cowan, is now remarried and lives in Leeds. It was easy for her to come to the crematorium this morning. And yet it was appropriate that someone from Carlin Beck, apart from the slow-voiced, rather solemn cobbler from Molethorpe Co-op, should be the only mourner outside the family. My father had felt at home in Carlin Beck. Though small, to him it had been a wider sphere. He would have liked to go on living there. Jenny still refers to him as 'Mister' (*tout court*). I know that she married early, and so I suppose she must be in her early fifties. She is still very handsome.

Two of her songs were *Il Bacio* and *Alice, where art thou? Hail, Smiling Morn* she learned to please my father and came round to give him its first performance at her parents' house on Christmas Day in 1923. It was a big, splendid voice. 'Brightly dawns upon me, dawns upon me, Heaven's gladsome ray. . . .' I remember the marvellous syncopation across the rapid waltz tempo. And I remember the delicious warbling and heaving as we approached the high note of 'My heart beating in my breast. . . .' It was at Carlin Beck that I first became interested in breasts, and I liked to think of the heart beating in Jenny's, thrilling as her voice thrilled, her breast white and delicately blue-veined like that which an even younger mother, a more distant relation of the Cowans, had shamelessly and delightfully uncovered to feed her baby in their kitchen during that first stay of ten days in their house.

To this day, Carlin Beck remains grief-coloured for me. It is difficult to believe that one small episode, though decisively placed so near the sensitive beginning of my two years there, together with the Sunday afternoon phobia, can account for the fact. I must, I fancy, have been influenced by my mother. The only thing she ever found to say in favour of the small, flat town was that her curtains didn't need washing as often there.

There were numerous things to be said in the place's favour. Not only from High Park, beyond the allotments to the north, but even, beyond the town, from Long Topping to the south, the sea was visible. Saltburn was a mere six miles away, Redcar not much more.

There were country walks near at hand in every direction.

A few weeks after those ten days, I started school not in Carlin Beck but at the Grange in Hinderholme. At school, there seemed to be no question of my presence there being only temporary. At home, my mother mentioned Carlin Beck only when she received my father's letters. I began to feel that the danger had passed. My father would never find a house. The move would not take place.

On Monday morning, the 14th of October, 1923, my mother told me that my father would be spending Thursday night at home. The front-room suite was to go to the auction rooms to-morrow. Mr Taylor, the General Manager at Carlin Beck, was lending us the Co-op removal van, which would appear on Friday morning. My father and I would travel north in the cab of this van with the driver, while Marjorie and my mother went to Carlin Beck by train. Our furniture was to be installed in the front room and two of the bedrooms at the Cowans, where we should go on living until a builder from Redcar had built us our own house in Nannygoat Park, a piece of land towards the allotments, where the miners trained their whippets and upon which they kept goats tethered.

It was a bit like this morning. That morning, we waited for the removal van. This morning, George Binns and I, wearing our black ties, waited for Uncle Arthur and the cobbler. My mother in a black frock, my sister wearing as many black trimmings as she could manage, waited for the undertakers' men in their top hats.

That morning, the taxi came at eleven o'clock. Taxis were a type of vehicle which had normally figured in our lives only twice a year, at the time of our departure for and return from our summer holidays. That year, there had also been the taxi which brought me home from the fever hospital in February, eight months before. A taxi was needed on October 18th, 1923, because my mother was taking bed-linen with her by train, so that she could air it before my father and I reached Carlin Beck with the beds. She was also taking Marjorie's cot, which, folded flat and much tied up with string, would go in the guard's van. It was my sister's third birthday.

When the taxi came, the van had not yet appeared. It had been scheduled to leave Carlin Beck in the small hours and reach us in time for a late breakfast.

'Are you sure you can manage, Alfred?' said my mother.

'Oh, we s' be all right,' said my father. 'Shan't we, lad?'

'I expect so,' said I, my round face, I feel sure, exhibiting no enthusiastic concurrence.

From her doorstep, next door but one below, Mrs Solace said:

'Nay, don't fret, Ethel. I'll see they both get a good dinner.'

'Grandma' Booth appeared at her door, above the passage.

'Ee, you're off then, Mrs Atha,' she said, 'I *shall* be sorry.'

Other people appeared. As my mother and Marjorie were getting into the taxi, the van came in sight at the bottom of Radcliffe Road.

'Well, I never!' said my mother.

She hesitated.

'Nay, you'd better go, Ethel,' said my father. 'There's nought else you can do, lass.'

'Well, good-bye,' said 'Grandma' Booth.

'Be good!' said Mrs Schofield, from across the road.

'Behave yourself!' said Mrs Jagger, who was passing.

These were two common forms of valediction in that neighbourhood.

'I shall be writing to you, Ethel,' said my mother to Mrs Solace.

'Grandma' Walker appeared.

'Nay, are you flitting, Mrs Atha?' she said. 'I didn't know. Eh, I'm fair sorry.'

'Grandma' Walker, who lived next door below, *had* known. Her mind was going.

With a ting-a-ling of the meter and a clashing of gears the taxi had turned and gone, Marjorie's cot on top. The van rumbled up and engaged its mighty brakes. The driver got out, blocked his wheels and fastened the doors back.

'Good morning, Mr Dadd,' said my father.

The driver nodded.

'You've had your breakfast, I expect?'

The driver did not answer.

'I forgot,' said my father. 'He's very hard of hearing, is Mr Dadd.'

'He'd tell us,' I said, 'if he hadn't had his breakfast.'

'You don't know,' said my father. 'Deaf folk can be very peculiar.'

Mr Dadd was throwing loose rolls of canvas into the roadway. Then he slid out a pair of iron-heeled runners.

Jumping down, he looked my father in the eyes, nodded as though affirmatively and led the way into the house that was still for a moment ours.

The van stood nearly as high as the house. From the roof-tops over the way, the weak autumn sun had slanted down upon our uncurtained windows and upon the leaves and the few last buds of the Dorothy Perkins climber. Now they lay mercifully in shadow.

My father and Mr Dadd reappeared with the sewing-machine. I held the wooden gate open. Mr Dadd, backing out, momentarily unbalanced and stuck his foot in the garden soil on a plant of love-lies-bleeding. The white-scoured doorstep and the scrubbed flags were soon in a state it would have broken my mother's heart to see. Aspidistra stand, music cabinet, zinc bath full of jams and pickles, rolled stair-carpet, gate-legged table, stood absurdly side by side upon the causeway.

'Do you want t' lad i' t' van, Mr Dadd?' said my father.

The removal man did not answer.

'He can't hear,' I said.

My father touched Mr Dadd's arm, pointed at me and then at the back of the van.

'Do you want him up there?' he said.

The removal man shook his head. For the first time, he opened his mouth.

'Piano,' he said.

Then he looked about him in every direction. This eventuality had been foreseen. I went through the passage to get Mr Mellor or Frank, both of whom were on night shift that week. On the way back, I noticed the clothes props, clamped against the garden wall on the passage side. I opened the back gate and stepped on the grass to get them. I put them down and went up three stone steps and in at the back door.

The coconut matting was up. The bare, concrete floor of the scullery now struck its chill through to the mind. The shiny, buff-painted walls were damp as if it had been Monday, washing day, not Friday. I should never again come home at tea-time on Tuesday to the smell of hot loaves and tea-cakes spread out on that table. There would never be sarsaparilla boiling again in the copper, or, if there was, it would not be I who drank it to cool my blood. Not that my blood needed cooling at the moment.

Frank Mellor had gone through the passage. There was a great shuffling and grunting in the front room, as he and my father and Mr Dadd made their combined assault upon the piano.

At twelve o'clock, the buzzer at the engineering works went. At a quarter past twelve, Brian Solace appeared at the top of Radcliffe Road. He did not hurry, but soon he was standing beside me. The van was almost loaded, the house almost empty.

'Are you glad you're off?' said Brian Solace.

'No,' said I.

Mrs Solace had come to her door again.

'We'd better go and wash us hands,' said Brian.

I went next door but one. My father followed. Mrs Solace took the removal man's dinner out to him.

By a little after two, the house was empty, and we had gone, driving first into the centre of Hinderholme, then turning left up Kirkgate and bearing right past St. Patrick's, past the Grange.

Once his engine was running Mr Dadd could hear perfectly. It was my father and I who had difficulty in making conversation over this vibrant thunder. We skirted Bradford and Harrogate, lumbered through Ripon to Northallerton and bore eastward into the Cleveland hills. It had long been dark by the time we reached Carlin Beck. When the van stopped outside the Cowans' house the first thing I noticed was that, somewhere up the road, children were singing carols. Yet it was still nearly three weeks to Bonfire Day.

Then it was Monday morning. At ten minutes to nine, there were fewer than a hundred boys scattered in their little groups about the sweeping concrete path, the verges of the football field, the rough grass practice-pitch and the cobbles leading up to the back entrance (the front entrance being out of bounds, to preserve the residential amenities of the school-house). The contingents by train from seaside and market towns and villages round about would not have arrived yet. Those from Middlesbrough came in after morning prayers.

I hoped to see the son of the gas manager, who was a Hinderholme man and whose family I had met in August. He did not seem to be about. Nor could I discover the features of 'Boy' Allendale. I approached one of the more studious-looking older boys and told him that I was new and that I supposed I ought to start off by seeing Mr Allendale. This boy (one of very few in long trousers, a garment to which school-boys took much later in those days) was of the opinion that the Boss would not appear until the school was assembled for prayers and that, as his study was in the school-house, I could not wait outside that. I had therefore better stay out here until prayers were over when he (this boy) would try to find means of informing the Boss of my presence. If he failed (he did fail), I could personally accost the Boss on his way out from prayers.

A bell rang. The boys who were gathered near the entrance pushed their way in, while others made their way up the cobbles at speeds proportionate to the distances they were away from all this Early English architecture. The whole area was deserted. Then Mr Allendale himself appeared. For so heavy-shouldered, big-bellied a man, his legs were thin. He wore both gown and mortar-board, with a shiny grey suit and light-tan brogue shoes, rubber-soled. As he padded past (at great speed for so top-heavy a man) he glanced at me (his pale eyes baggy and a little bloodshot) and frowned, but said nothing. Two late-comers, with red faces, turned the corner off the concrete path and panted up the cobbles, their satchels thumping their backs.

There was a mass knocking and scraping from within, as no doubt the school rose to its feet at the Boss's entrance, then a chord on the piano and a hymn with which I was unfamiliar. Where I stood, my back to the school-building, I had the door through which everybody had entered on my left and, on my right, the arch off which the school-house door opened and from which the Boss had emerged. Immediately beyond the school entrance, an outhouse projected, with its own door. This was doubtless the cloakroom. The view before me, past where the cobbles ended, was of half the football field, seen from one end, and, to the right of this, a good deal less than half of the cricket field, stepped up a yard or so from the level of the football

107

field, a wooden pavilion with its back to the line of junction. The foreground was broken by trees and by a long, creosoted shed.

As the hymn ended and the murmuring of a prayer began, a final late-comer, in a state of acute physical distress flitted by me with a wild stare, stopped for a moment to listen to the sounds from within and tip-toed into what I took to be the cloakroom. Into sight immediately afterwards came the first three of a group of some twenty boys quite unhurried. They would be the Middlesbrough contingent.

A further shuffling and banging had arisen within, and Mr Allendale came swiftly out of the main entrance. He halted and glanced curiously at me, as I turned to him and touched my cap.

'New boy, eh?'

He looked about him for somebody to whom he could pass on the problem I presented, as though his breakfast might be getting cold. Then he beckoned me to follow him, turned into the arch and opened a door set in the near side of it.

'Wait in there,' he said, 'What did you say your name was?'

I told him.

'Right,' said Mr Allendale. 'I'll . . . I'll see you in a minute.'

I entered a classroom and stood by the master's desk. Boys older than myself began to file in and take their places. Seeing that the Boss was not there, they moved from desk to desk, talked with increasing freedom and did their best not to keep noticing me. I was clearly a new boy. The badge on my cap was dazzling, the yellow and green of my tie had not yet run in the wash. Though I was a bit on the chubby side and though, in an area of Scandinavian fairness, I seemed a bit red-haired, there was nothing grotesque about my appearance. I was a boy of average stature, wearing a short-trousered, navy-blue suit of moderate newness, first-rate material and unexceptionable cut.

A boy sitting in a position from which he could see through the open door gesticulated anxiously, and the room was quiet. Mr Allendale came in.

'I don't see many books open,' he said.

The sudden flicking over of pages caused a perceptible breath of air in the room. This continued. Nobody seemed to know at what page his book ought to be open. I saw that the books were in fact Bibles.

'Well, Bowles, old man, do you know where you'd got to?' said the Boss to a boy in the front row.

'Yes, sir,' said Bowles.

'H'm,' said the Boss, 'you're a better man than I am, Gunga Din.'

'It was the marriage feast at Cana, sir,' called out another boy.

'And what did *Ah Lawd* do there?' said the Boss.

There rose a forest of hands.

'*Ah Lawd* rendered sterling service at Cana,' said the Boss. 'You, Read . . .'

'Yes, sir?'

'Who was Gunga Din?'

The forest of hands had withered. Now, as though the rains had come, it sprang up again.

'A water-carrier, sir,' said Read.

'Near enough, Read, near enough,' said the Boss.

'At any rate he gave his life like a man, when the moment came.

> 'An' for all 'is dirty 'ide
> 'E was white, clear white, inside
> When 'e went to tend the wounded under fire!

'We don't judge people by the colour of their skins, Bowles, do we?'

'No, sir,' said Bowles.

'A good thing, too, Bowles,' said the Boss, 'After all, *Ah Lawd* was a Jew. Eh, Salkeld? Are *you* white, clear white inside, eh?'

'I don't know, sir,' said Salkeld unhappily.

'Gunga Din,' said the Boss, 'died serving the Widow. Who was the Widow, Hallam?'

'His mother, sir,' Hallam ventured hopefully.

'His *mother*?' said the Boss. '*Whose* mother?'

Hallam switched his guess.

'*Ah Lawd's* mother, sir,' he said.

Mr Allendale smote his forehead and groaned. He declaimed:

> 'So I'll meet 'im later on
> At the place where 'e is gone—
> Where it's always double drill and no canteen;
> 'E'll be squattin' on the coals
> Givin' drink to poor damned souls,
> An' I'll get a drink in hell from Gunga Din!

'Like Dives and Lazarus. Right, find Dives and Lazarus.

> 'Matthew, Mark, Luke and John,
> *Acts* and *Romans* follow on . . . '

'Well, old man,' he now said to me, 'what have *you* been up to?'

'Nothing, sir,' I said.

A reflective pause.

'No, that's it, you're the new boy. Tell me your name again, old man.'

I told him. I told him what form he had said, weeks ago, I was to be in. I told him that I had not yet been issued with either exercise books or text-books.

He fumbled beneath his gown, pulled out a bunch of keys on a chain and, selecting one, opened a cupboard at the back of the classroom. The lower shelves contained plaster casts of cylinders, pyramids, a Corinthian capital. From a shelf above these, the Boss sorted out a number of exercise books and gave them to me.

'Did you say "text-books"?' he asked.

'Yes, sir.'

'Oh, we don't provide those, old man,' he said. 'You'll have to get them.'

He gave me the name of a stationer in the High Street.

'What form did I say you were in?'

'Form Two,' I told him.

'Yes,' he said, 'well, that's on the other side of this wall. You'll find your way round. When you see Mr Clapp, ask him to get one of his boys to make you out a list of all the books you'll need.'

Mr Clapp was short, fat, of a florid complexion and dark colouring, hawk-nosed and with a head which sloped away at the back, the crown apparently tonsured. His gait was stately. He strutted like a bantam cock, his feet turned sharply out. On the desks were Latin primers, a type of book with which I was not yet familiar. Some of the boys glanced sideways at me, without raising their heads. E. Furneaux Clapp strutted between the rows, sprinkling the floor with disinfectant of a pale-green colour from a medicine bottle.

He lifted his nose in the air.

'I mix it myself,' he said.

And he explained to me that the purpose of the disinfectant was to combat the horrid diseases the tainted breath of Form Two must otherwise infect him with. It also, he said, somewhat counteracted the offence their crowded bodies gave his nostrils.

'What's your name?' he said, ' "Crawford"?'

'No, sir,' I said.

'Ah,' said he, looking at my hair, 'I thought you were one of Crawford's ginger nuts. What *is* your name?'

I told him.

' "Attar"?' he said. 'Of roses, I presume. I'll go and put it down in the register.'

He asked me where I came from. I told him. He admitted that it was at least a town, though not on quite the scale of Liverpool. He supposed that not all the people in Hinderholme were Yahoos like those in the neighbourhood in which it was at present his misfortune to teach.

A boy with a big, red nose was contemplating me at his ease. Mr Clapp turned on him.

'Ablative,' he demanded, 'of *nasum*?'

Tribick, whose voice had already broken, did not know. A soft-featured boy with a club foot told him.

'Ovid,' said Clapp, 'was blest with a conk like yours, Tribick. He was called "Ovidius *naso*".'

Tribick was a big, easy-going fellow. He grinned contentedly, and one felt that under other circumstances he might have fetched E. Furneaux Clapp a clip on the ear and playfully knocked him down. In that case, Mr Clapp would at once have bounded up again, like a celluloid Humpty-Dumpty with lead-weighted base. Tribick's father was a publican.

By the mid-morning break, I had picked up the names of one or two of my form-mates. For instance, the club-footed boy was Pallister, and there were two Smiths, known as Smith II and Smith III, brothers. My memory of Petch shows him always loose-lipped, grinning with anticipation of trouble, permanently agitated with gregarious excitement. He would be one of those who thronged about me at break on that first morning. There were also boys from the Boss's own form. The authority both on me and on Hinderholme was the gas manager's son, who seemed, however, not to be a leader of opinion. He knew that my father worked at the Co-op and that I was a scholarship boy.

The bell went. There was history with Mr Lloyd, a strongly built, black-haired Welshman with dark, penetrating eyes, an impediment in his speech and a hare-lip or at any rate a deformed or damaged lip, upon which grew the kind of moustache one much later associated with the not-yet-heard-of Hitler.

I went back to the Cowans' with my list of books, which included not only Latin, French, mathematical and scientific text-books but a *Book of Common Prayer* and a *Hymns Ancient and Modern*. As I had foreseen, my father was very much put-out by this list. He glanced significantly at my mother and chewed his moustache. The fault, he seemed to be indicating, was mine, but he would say nothing on this occasion.

At the end of a long afternoon, there were evening prayers. A psalm was sung in the manner in which psalms presumably were sung at Church, to me a very odd manner. The other boys had brought their caps into prayers, so as to be the more quickly away. I went back to Mr Clapp's form-room to get mine out of the desk.

A number of boys were still there on the cobbles, whispering excitedly. I did not look at them. I wanted to get home. I skirted the group. They had all turned to face me. I smiled at them.

Then a heavy shoulder against mine tipped me off my balance, and I was in the middle of the group, who were manhandling me into the cloakroom.

Voices said:

'Shut the door.'

And it became almost dark. Something cold and wet was dabbed on my right cheek, and, wrenching one hand free and touching my face, I saw that my finger-tips, as my arm was pulled away again, were black. Then I was firmly pinioned, and a boy whose features I did not distinguish, if only because I was turning my head this way and that (but they *could* have been Petch's features), was dipping a rag into a tin of boot-polish and plastering my face with it in what my efforts to dodge turned into a series of sharp jabs. My nose started bleeding.

The whole operation lasted no more than a minute or two, and I was presently let go, the whole group at once scattering, so that I was left alone in that cloakroom, which also contained a row of wash-basins and of which the door now again stood open. I was hot. My hands trembled. It would have been difficult to say whether I merely panted or whether it was a kind of abortive sob which so disturbed my breathing.

I found a fragment of soap. I had a handkerchief. And there was a dirty roller-towel behind the door. I made some effort to clean my face, then looked around for my cap. I could not find it.

Aware that I looked a sight and that I could hardly go along the high street as I was, I tried to find side-streets that would take me to the Cowans' road. I blundered more than once, and by the time I reached the Cowans' it was dark, my parents had finished their tea, and the blood had clotted in my nostrils, so that I no longer sniffed. My father was on the point of returning to the Shop.

It was, of course, my mother who (with a little help from Mrs Cowan) did most of the exclaiming, but it was my father's contribution which brought on panic. He would, he stated, have to go round to school in the morning and see Mr Allendale.

I begged him not to.

'They'd reckon I was a sneak,' I said.

'A what, lad?' asked my father.

'A sneak,' I said.

'Oh. . . .'

My father had never read *The Magnet* or *The Gem*. Codes of honour which had filtered down by literary channels from the public schools meant nothing to him.

'It's called "ragging",' I explained. 'They always do

that at this kind of school. They do it to everybody.'

'They must use a lot of blacking,' said my father. 'Just look at your suit and your collar. You've lost your new cap, an' all. We can't have that, you know.'

'I'll find my cap in the morning,' I said.

As I had no text-books, there was no homework I could do. As soon as I was properly cleaned up and no longer hungry, I went into the front room, sat on a chair-arm I managed to clear by the window and stared out into the gaslit street.

A few people passed. I did not know them. A few doors away, two children were singing carols. That in itself was a melancholy fact. They should have been collecting for Guy Fawkes' day. On Saturday morning, they had been round with their half-filled basins, selling blackberries, which they called brambles. In August, they had come round with bilberries or, as they called them, blueberries.

If I asked him, no doubt the gas manager's son would tell me whether, when the school year began a month ago, all the new boys had been ragged in this way. I did not think I would ask him. He must have had a good idea what was afoot, and he had not warned me. I knew, in any case, what the answer would be. With so many boys living elsewhere and leaving early to catch trains, wholesale ragging would have to be done entirely by Carlin Beck boys. They could not have managed it. Older Brotton boys would have stood up for Brotton new boys, Loftus older boys for Loftus new boys and so on. Either they had taken a dislike to me personally, or their tradesmen parents had murmured about the Co-op and about scholarship boys. Or perhaps they were cowards and bullies. Perhaps the sole explanation was that I had come to the school alone.

Trains apart, only a Carlin Beck boy could have got a tin of boot-polish at dinner-time. I had not recognised any of my assailants for certain. From subsequent knowledge of their characters and circumstances, my guess now would be that Petch had provided the boot-polish and that he had been put up to it by an older boy, but I do not think that I reached this conclusion while I was at Carlin Beck.

It was the worst moment of my life to date. In fact it was the only very bad moment. I had not much cared for my first night at the fever hospital, but at least I had not expected that to go on for more than a week or two. There might be no end to this. I was an exile in a strange land. I had accepted the fact of exile before I arrived. But I was also an outcast. That had been decided on my arrival.

A hot, viscous tear formed in each eye and stiffly overflowed. Two bare-footed children shuffled past the window peering in. I drew back, and in the dark room they could not see me. They began to sing at the Cowans' door.

And so, for the next few days, my poor father had two of us weeping, myself in the furniture-cluttered front room during the evening, my mother in bed at night (I did not know this at the time). I got through that week all right, and on Saturday there was a respite. The next day, I ought to have started Sunday school. At the Co-op, they were all Methodists. The idea was that Charlie, my father's lively and charming assistant, should take me to the chapel attended also by the general manager and the secretary (and, formerly, by the Cowans). My father may have thought that I had seen enough unfamiliar faces for one week, or he may already have toyed with the notion of breaking down anti-Co-op feeling at the Church end of the town, having perhaps also heard that few Grammar School boys went to Chapel, if any. The gas manager's son was in the choir (and in the boy scouts) at the church, whose rector, a bearded Scot, Mr Hamilton, was an extravagantly popular figure in the town, through which he strode clung to by adoring little girls.

At any rate, that first Sunday, I went nowhere. This was a relief, but it laid up for me a recurrent misery. I *never* went to Sunday school in Carlin Beck. Sometimes, in the afternoon, my father sent me out to post a letter. The post office lay in a turning off the far side of the high street, towards the beck.

I went out in dread. The very small number of people I passed in the street and the great many sitting behind their lace curtains were, I knew, all looking at me, tight-lipped.

To themselves or to each other, exchanging significant glances, they were saying:

'Why is that boy not at Sunday school?'

There was a more rigid sabbatarianism in Carlin Beck than in Hinderholme. At Linfootlock, my father had worked in his allotment on Sunday mornings. At Carlin Beck, Mr Cowan had warned him from the beginning that he ought not to.

While the milder weather lasted, the tension of Sundays might be relaxed by an expedition to Saltburn for the day. In winter, all I could do was stay indoors on

Sunday afternoon, hoping that my father would either have no letters to post or that he would give them to me before dinner.

ONCE OUT OF TOWN, WE DROVE AT A BOWLING PACE ALL the way to Leeds. But for the last mile, that was the way I went for some weeks in the autumn of 1929 on the pillion of Bee Webb's motor-bike, a powerful 9 h.p. Raleigh.

After that, I commuted by train. So, in the end, did Bee, at any rate in winter. His real name was Sidney Webb. His parents were Fabians. He was brought up a high-minded atheist and went to the Socialist Sunday School in Ellen Brig. He was called 'Sidney' after the Bloomsbury Webbs. He had once explained this to us. He was called 'Sidney,' he said, after Sidney and Beatrice Webb. So we called him first 'Beatrice', then 'Beatie', then 'Bee'. He and I first became thick in IV A at the Grange. I realised that his mother was the Ma Webb, a widow, who'd taught Standard VII at Linfootlock. She used to give them lessons in Esperanto. I can't think what Arthur Lumb and Freddie Fischer made of that. I dare say Wilfred Helliwell made something of it, but that it served him to little purpose once he had started working in the quarries.

In my year, there were five of us from the Grange and one from another high school in Hinderholme, a co-educational one to which Mildred Walsh and Karen had also gone three weeks before I went to Carlin Beck.

He did Physics. Two of my Grange contemporaries did Gas Engineering. Bee Webb and another, who lived in at Devonshire Hall (his home lay outside Hinderholme, and formerly he had commuted by train to school), did French. A year before we left school, Bee and I had done *cours de vacances* together at the Collège Sophie-Berthelot in Calais.

I have not seen any of these men since I went down from Leeds fifteen years ago. Only Pargeter. He also lived in at Devonshire Hall.

Pargeter came from further north even than Carlin Beck. Stockton, I fancy, or the Quaker town, Darlington. A funny thing about accents. With a man like Pargeter, you only know in a general kind of way that he comes from somewhere between the Trent and the Tyne. Among schoolboys, you can tell within twenty or thirty miles.

Certainly, you can tell which Riding they come from. Of course, the great division runs across Yorkshire, at somewhere about the latitude of York. The speech of Cleveland has more in common with that of Cumberland than with that of the West Riding. Vocabulary, idiom, pronunciation and inflexion are all quite different. Hardly a vowel-sound is the same. Also, it may be, within our different geographical contexts, I spoke more broadly than most of the boys at a predominantly fee-paying school not without social pretensions locally.

On my first day at Carlin Beck Grammar School, I perceived only too well that the other boys spoke differently from me. It was some weeks before it became clear to me that I must therefore speak differently from them.

Each form had a monitor for the week, whose duty it was to ascertain and call out the names of those absent from his form that day. This must have been at an *ad hoc* assembly either after the mid-morning break or at the beginning of the afternoon.

Form One sat at the back, the Fifth at the front. There was nothing higher than the Fifth. There were only five masters in the school.

On my first day as monitor, a boy called Huntley was away, and so, when Form Two was called on to answer, I sang out:

'Huntley absent, sir.'

From his desk at the front, Mr Allendale said:

'I beg your pardon?'

The school got ready to laugh.

'Huntley absent, sir,' I repeated.

' "Oontleh"?' said the Boss. ' "Obsunt"? Never heard of 'em.'

The school laughed.

'Look, West Riding,' said the Boss, 'You'd better try that again.'

The school held its breath.

'Hantlee ebsint, sir,' I said, as it sounded to me.

'Come again.'

'Hantlee ebsint, sir.'

'That's better, old man.'

Thereafter, I became 'West Riding' for a while, but this was cumbersome. Clapp went on calling me 'Crawford', but he was not a popular man, and the boys rarely adopted his witticisms. I never quite settled down to a nickname at Carlin Beck. My surname itself was held to be opprobrious enough.

The Boss was popular, though his temper was known to be uncertain. Sarcasm and verbal torture were not at all his line in a general way, though he did pick on two boys for militaristic reasons. A greengrocer, one of only two boys, apart from myself, whom I remember living at the miners' end of the town, conscientiously objected to his son parading with the O.T.C. Perhaps he was a Quaker from Darlington twenty miles away.

His son, a sardonic boy of dewlapped ugliness, was, however, a humorist and a philosopher, so that he was able to make light of the Boss's scorn. Not so Schumm. A quiet, red-haired boy of German parentage, Schumm clearly represented, for the Boss, his ancient enemy, the Hun. He pronounced this boy's name not as 'Shoom' but always, with savage contempt, as 'Scum'. Whether this preyed on the boy's mind or, reported at home, roused indignation in his father's breast, I do not know, but I seem to remember that Schumm left shortly after my arrival at the school.

Then possibly I was the reddest-headed boy in the school. In Hinderholme, I had never been thought red-headed. My hair had sometimes been described as 'sandy', though no fuss was made of the fact. Even sandiness was bleached out of it by the Rhineland sun seven years later. Perhaps there was more red hair in Hinderholme.

I did not mind being called 'West Riding'. That made me seem less, not more, alien. It appointed me to a place. I was a foreigner, but of known and respectable provenance.

Mr Clapp frequently denounced Carlin Beck, its inhabitants and the whole of Cleveland. As a comer-in from more civilised parts, I was supposed to back up his statements.

'Isn't that so, Crawford?' he would say.

Or:

'Crawford, am I right?'

Mere truthfulness would often compel me to say:

'No, sir.'

Then Clapp would turn on me and describe Hinderholme to the others. It was, he declared, a town so precipitous that the only vehicles able to negotiate its streets were goat-carts. You came, he said, out of the station into Union Square, and there they were, lined up, no taxis, no trams, but only goat-carts.

'Am I right, Crawford?'

'No, sir.'

As it happens, the immediate vicinity of Union Square and the station is one of the levellest parts of Hinderholme. It is in fact a precipitous town. I had not thought so until Clapp pointed it out. I had simply thought Carlin Beck a flat town. I had not been in a flat town before. Scarborough is not flat. Once you get outside it, Blackpool has cliffs. That the houses in both were made of brick, I had supposed a seaside oddity till I went to Carlin Beck, which, after all, was not far from the sea.

It seemed to me normal that a railway, in order to avoid degenerating into a series of switchbacks, should ride across elevated viaducts like the one striding the Helm between Molethorpe and Mallalieu Park, that the same railway should cross Ram Lane, and another the hill up to Holt End, by iron bridges and that both railways should thunder between the stone walls of deep cuttings before they plunged into tunnels from which they emerged into Hinderholme station. Steep concrete paths, iron bridges, uncountable steps and the thousand windowed mills along the Hinder, seemed to me what a town was. It seemed to me natural that innumerable mill chimneys should rise out of a town and that, wherever you stood, a hill like Cowl Hill, with its Victorian watch-tower, should stand to the south and that nearer bits of unbuildable green hillside should visibly defy industry and such builders as Law Barraclough.

There is still a hint of cream in the tower on Cowl Hill at a thousand feet, but in town the older buildings are caked black. The house I was born in is only a year older than I am. When I left it at the age of twelve, it must have been much darkened already, though I continued to think of it as yellow and glittering with quartz particles in the sun, washed by the heavy downpours of July rain.

During a July downpour, my mother would say:

'That's right, David! Send it down!'

David *pluviosus* was, I dare say, the only pagan figure in her pantheon, though, when tired out at the end of washing day, she once passed her hands over her face in this house and said:

'Eh, if I have to come back, it won't be for not toiling, I'm sure.'

I like stone. I am a lithophile. I like the idea of a land clothed with buildings dug out of it. The day before yesterday, as the train curved eastward through Staleybridge, it was not altogether because of my father that I felt a disgraceful prickling behind eyes before which a brick landscape changed into a stone one.

Industry alone is not much defacement. Pushed up against the Pennines and built of local sandstone across the junction of two small, turbulent rivers, Hinderholme is quite a handsome town. At any rate, on three sides. It degenerates as the land flattens towards Leeds. It is years, ten or eleven, since I saw any part of the centre of Leeds. I did not see it this morning. No doubt it has improved.

But it is Carlin Beck I must think of, not Leeds, and, for the moment, E. Furneaux Clapp. He had a room in the school-house. He was related to some famous scientist, Jeans or Rutherford. Indeed, he gave us to understand that all the Clapps were prominent scientists, except himself. What dreadful fate had compelled him to be a schoolmaster, he could not imagine.

He was one of that tribe of rogue schoolmasters who stimulate because they never stick to the syllabus, but let in echoes from another world. He was scandalously amusing on O.T. Divinity and really understood English grammar, syntax and prosody, which not every teacher of English does. I owe him my parts of speech. I owe him *Chevy Chase* and *Sir Patrick Spens*. To scan, he gave us things like:

> Little Willie had a monkey,
> Climbing up a yellow stick;
> And, when he licked the paint all off
> It made him very sick.

One of the many subjects we had Clapp for was woodwork. This took place after break on Friday mornings. The carpenter's shop, as the woodwork shed was called, lay beyond the Armoury, among trees. We were making pipe-racks in yellow walnut. As we planed, sandpapered, drilled, chiselled and glued, Clapp himself worked at the shaping of a flat piece of wood about a yard long and four inches broad. This was to be a new and improved instrument of corporal punishment. He brought it into the form room on a Monday morning, beautifully polished. The ordinary cane, he explained affected an insufficient area of the person. This would produce a maximum of immediate pain with a minimum risk of permanent injury.

'Stand up, Petch,' he commanded.

Hanging his head and goggling with mock terror, Petch rose.

'Bend over the desk.'

Petch did so, his head turned to where his friends sat, winking at them, dribbling on the floor. Clapp lifted up the tail of Petch's jacket and smoothed out the seat of his trousers.

'There must be no folds or creases,' he explained.

Petch now broke into a sweat of real terror. Clapp swung his arm back mightily. The instrument began its rapid descent. Petch squealed. The instrument slowed and came to rest gently on his bottom.

We sat slouched in our desks, glad of the diversion. Clapp raised his invention in the air again and slapped it thunderously down on Tribick *naso*'s desk. Tribick grinned tolerantly.

As a bachelor, Mr Clapp had a room in the schoolhouse. Alone among the masters, he did not attend either morning or evening prayers. He was presumed an atheist. When we came out of morning prayers, we generally found him in his form room, tubbily but haughtily sprinkling the floor with disinfectant, a meditative exercise during which he would work out his ways of tormenting us.

He did not often torment me. If anything, he favoured me a bit. And in fact, during all that remained of the two years my family spent in Carlin Beck, nothing else happened to me that I found particularly unpleasant. After a while, even the Sunday-afternoon letter-posting dread faded, because we took to attending church in the evening. And yet both my mother and I continued to yearn for the familiar industrial climate of Hinderholme and for our former friends.

For my part, I never made close friends in Carlin Beck. Smith III was my best friend, but he went home at week-ends, and, during the summer term, he was removed from me in the evenings by the fact that both he and his brother were quite exceptional cricketers (the result, I understood, of their father's coaching) and were both put in the school team, which kept them busy practising at the nets. I became very solitary, partly, as I felt, from necessity, partly from choice.

On summer evenings and on Saturday afternoons, I sat and read in a part of my father's allotment which he had allocated to me and which was perfectly secluded, since it lay between a tall hedge and two rows of sweet peas, beyond which were the runner beans. Beyond the allotments, the land dipped through fields to a stream and then rose again to the larch plantation through which one reached the top of the hill known as High Park, which had in fact once been a wood but among whose stumps now blew a profusion of foxgloves and willow-herb, burdock, forget-me-nots, bluebells and marsh marigolds. As the approach to High Park lay at the miners' end of the town, I never met Grammar School boys up there. The book under my arm might be *The Last Days of Pompeii*, *Quo Vadis* or *Ben Hur*, *The Talisman*, *The Hunchback of Notre Dame*, *Eugene Aram*. There might also be a notebook in which I tried to write a story about pirates sailing among the islands of the Caribbean, a country of the mind which latterly had replaced the Holy Land, Sherwood Forest and Tarzan's Africa.

I had got the books in sixpenny book-of-the-film editions from Woolworth's at Easter, when I was allowed to go to Hinderholme for a week and stayed in Bradford Road with Uncle Nathan, A'ntie Beulah and Gertie. I went up to see Brian Solace in Linfootlock. The Wreck was already built over. The houses in Radcliffe Road had shrunk. In six months, they had become small, blackened boxes. I wondered how I had managed to live twelve years in one without any sense of constriction.

At Carlin Beck, one game of football took place in the summer term. This was an annual event. An old boy of the school, a ship-owner in Middlesbrough, brought over a team of Lascars who played barefoot against a school team which included two of the masters, the Welsh History master and the tall, dark, bespectacled young Maths teacher, a hare-like right wing. The school team played in the usual studded boots, and one feared for those poor brown feet.

For the first time, at Carlin Beck, my father began to exert himself in public life. Despite his friendship with the gas manager, his great ambition was to see the town lighted by electricity. A minor ambition was to stock grammar-school caps and ties at the Co-op. It may have been with the idea of furthering this ambition that we started going to church on Sunday evenings. It may, on the other hand, have been with the idea of procuring more contentment both for me and for my mother. She had not made many friends. Perhaps he hoped that she would make some at church. He did not know about my Sunday-afternoon dread, but perhaps thought that I might join the choir in which the gas manager's son sang, and the boy scouts, to which the gas manager's son also belonged (and where, by his account, there took place nameless orgies, into the precise nature of which I did not enquire). It was also the case that the bearded Scottish rector, Mr Hamilton, was a man of conspicuous amiability, not in the least parsonical in his manner.

I approved wholeheartedly of this churchgoing. I liked the bells especially (St. Oswald's had a full chime of eight). True, you don't have to go to church to hear church bells, but it is different when their summons is addressed to oneself, informing one, across a whole town, that it is time to swallow one's last cup of tea or quickly reach the end of a chapter and mark the place. There is also that pleasant moment when, being early and having leant forward, counted ten and sat up again, you still hear a single bell directly overhead and wait for the organ to play and the vestry door to open and the choir appear in their surplices, including the gas manager's son with his yellow hair standing on end.

Compared with Wesleyan chapels, churches were

evidently chilly, dark and uncomfortable places, but perhaps for that reason the service was kept short, and in summer one did not mind all that bare stone, while there were cushions provided to kneel on so that people could now and then relieve their cramped limbs by a change of position. I thought it odd to repeat the same prayers every week, but perhaps Mr Hamilton's power of invention was exhausted. And so, quite happily, I stood up, sat down, knelt and said that I had done those things which I ought not to have done and left undone those things which I ought to have done and that there was no health in me and that I believed in the holy Catholic church, the communion of saints, the forgiveness of sins, the resurrection of the body and the life everlasting and ducked my head every time 'Ah Lawd' was referred to as Jesus Christ, and listened patiently to Mr Hamilton's brief, inoffensive sermons.

At the end of the summer term, I had a success at school. In addition to the form tests, a General Knowledge paper was set for the whole school, and (a sign, no doubt, of the advantages of an urban upbringing) I came out top.

When (with asides about the disquieting ignorance of boys in the Fifth) this astonishing result had been announced at afternoon assembly, the Boss said:

'Come on, chaps, let's give old West Riding a clap.'

This, so far as I could judge, they did with a good heart, at any rate the boys in the lower forms.

The builder from Redcar had bought land for four houses, but he proposed to build them only as the customer presented himself, and the other potential customers preferred to wait until they saw how we got on. For our house was being built of concrete blocks, and doubtful prognostication was rife.

Even my father began to say:

'Ay, that's the worst of a little place like this. Everybody knows too much about other folk's business.'

Even or, indeed, especially at working-class level, there had been some hostility to this building project. Nannygoat Park cannot have been common land in any legal sense, but we had certainly narrowed the tethering-space for goats and shortened the length of the course over which the miners, with flapping handkerchiefs and loud whistling, could train their whippets. The miners' wives, however, spoke up for my father, with whom they dealt at the Shop and who was further agitating on what they felt to be their own behalf (and against the interests of his friend, the gas manager) to get electricity brought into a town whose gas was provided by a private company, which could charge what it liked, with no rebate on the rates.

No sooner had we moved than my father took a second allotment. This he proposed to turn into a hen-run.

Once our sizeable back garden was dug and planted, he and I fenced round the second allotment with barrel-staves. Together, we built and creosoted coops. I bought myself sittings of the eggs of fancy breeds, such as Old English Pheasant Fowl and White Faverolles. I also kept rabbits, which gnawed their way out of the hutch I made for them and were chased around Nannygoat Park by the miners' whippets.

My father took up the construction of wireless sets, too. He made not only our own, from blue-prints given away with one of the new wireless weeklies, but also sets for sale at the Shop. Our kitchen became the scene of much drilling of ebonite panels and soldering of tinned wire to brass terminals. There were loathsome smells of burning ebonite and delicious smells of sizzling resin. I made a crystal-set on a piece of coarse wood, with a coil moulded on a hexagonal calf's-foot-jelly bottle and a condenser made up of alternating layers of tinfoil and waxed paper. With this, I listened to Newcastle.

On cold, autumn nights, newly hatched chicks were brought into the kitchen and dried off in boxes of straw on the cooling stove. Then the wireless parts were removed from the table. A clean *Daily Mail* or *North-Eastern Daily Gazette* was spread there. A paste of egg and crumbs was mixed in a saucer or special fine grain strewn on the paper itself. The pecking balls of yellow fluff filled the over-heated room with their pretty chirpings.

These shared pleasures brought me closer to my father than I had ever felt myself to be since first I sat on his knee and played with his watch. Not but that chickens have darker lessons to teach. As they grew older, we first picked out the males not by the form of their tail feathers but by the savagery with which they tore each other's combs and pecked at each other's eyes. Sometimes a mature hen-bird would sicken and sit moping in a corner, eyelids down, wings drooping, swaying on unsteady legs if she tried to rise. This behaviour would rouse the other birds to a brisk indignation. Each time they noticed their spoilsport sister, they would nip across and take a peck at her.

That autumn, churchgoing lapsed. Now that we no longer lived with the Cowans, there was nobody to leave my sister with. But also, now that we lived in a house of our own, the integration of ourselves into the community seemed less urgent. As for lighting, we had, for the moment, paraffin lamps. Damp came in through the concrete blocks, but a coat of some liquid cement cured that. By and large, there was contentment in the family.

Clapp was our form master not only in Form Two but in Form Three as well. When it was made known, in September, that we were going to have to put up with him for another year, we groaned. And yet he had never failed to keep our interest. The chief weakness at that school was the French. However, we read Erckmann-Chatrian's *Le Blocus*, a book I might otherwise never have come across, though later I was to know the Erckmann-Chatrian country pretty well.

We did *Le Blocus* with the Boss. We also got some of our Latin from him. He supervised our drawing of plaster casts on Thursday mornings, and last period on Thursday afternoons we had N.T. Divinity with him.

There was a Mrs Allendale whom we never saw. She was presumed an invalid. Certainly, the Boss was not altogether a happy man. He was moody, and he evidently drank. He made us learn Kipling's 'If . . .'. That was safe. It was safe, too, when he invoked the green eye of the little yellow god. When he got on to Dives and Lazarus, however, by way of Gunga Din 'givin' drink to poor damned souls', the Boss would become thoughtful and leave us. Then he would come in to evening prayers swaying slightly, glassy-eyed and smelling faintly of whisky. According to the gas manager's son, he was always drunk, too, when he deputised for Mr Hamilton and took a morning service at St. Oswald's.

The only time I saw him in a surplice was on Ascension Day, when the whole school went to church. I saw him now and then in khaki. On Armistice Day, we paraded in front of the church in cheese-cutter caps with the badge of the Green Howards, brass-buttoned tunics, short khaki trousers and, below our bare knees, puttees. The arms we ordered, shouldered, presented and reversed were old cavalry carbines. They were kept in the long, creosoted shed known as the Armoury, where also there were some B.S.A. ·22 rifles with which now and then we practised musketry and which we fired on a range laid out near the Priory ruins. A squad of the smartest of us (I was not included, but Smith III was) drilled intensively for some weeks before competing for a Lucas-Tooth shield, annually presented.

After the Armistice Day parade, a delightful institution was that, at the Boss's expense, still in our uniforms (except for cap and belt), we ate pork-pies and drank ginger beer in his form room. I suppose we did this, too, after a more impressive parade at which the Carlin Beck war memorial was unveiled. Like the felling of mill chimneys in Hinderholme, this public event was commemorated by a postcard on sale locally. My mother has such a postcard, upon which she has marked the back of my head with a cross. It looks like the back of any other head. We are presenting arms. The most impressive figure on the platform is, I suppose, a colonel of the Green Howards. Beside him is bearded and surpliced Mr Hamilton. The civilians are no doubt Lord Cleveland and the member for his constituency, at that time, I fancy, a Liberal and therefore his enemy.

Another public event, commemorated by postcards in early 1925, was the running aground at Saltburn, just by the pier, of a Dutch schooner with a cargo of China clay. When a high tide again floated this vessel, it went through the pier. A singing master came to the school one morning a week from Saltburn. He drove a thriving trade in the two glossy postcards, one showing the schooner before and one after it had gone through the pier.

At Easter, the Boss, together with the plump and wholly amiable Science master, took a party to London for the Empire Exhibition. We occupied a hut with bunks somewhere in the neighbourhood of Wembley. It was my first trip to London or anywhere south of the Trent. Of London I remember only Trafalgar Square and the embankment at Westminster. Of the Exhibition I remember Indian temples and Kaffir kraals, what seemed to me the sophistication of milk-and-soda at glass-fronted bars, the rodeo, cowboys lounging outside the stadium, chewing gum, talking to girls and, laconically, to us. Smith III was not on the expedition. The gas manager's son was. The Rev. G. L. M. Allendale, M.A., shed his dog-collar, wore a soft collar and tie. We found this odd, though we could not have said why.

At Whitsuntime, Grandad Sykes came to stay. He and I botanised over High Park and among the red-stained, newt-populated streams and 'blueberries' of Long Topping. I had supposed that area marvellous for a botanist, but Grandad Sykes said that the flora was more extensive round Hinderholme. This surprised me, though it was true that, within a mile or so of mills, I had never gone short of bluebells, streams to dam, yellow-striped bumble and red-tipped soldier bees to catch with cap or handkerchief on clover. The woods in the hollow to which the far side of Cowl Hill descends would have been white a month or two ago with wood anemones.

When Grandad Sykes had gone back to Holt End, where now there was only A'ntie Ada living with him, my mother said that she had not liked the look of him. I had failed to notice how thin and sallow he was, how easily tired and disinclined to eat.

I went to Hinderholme in the summer holidays, staying part of the time with Brian Solace and part with a boy with whom I had been friendly at the board school and who also went to the Wesleyans, where a tennis club had just been started. That was when I saw Arthur Lumb, former undisputed champion of the Radcliffe Roaders and Springland Streeters, now trimmed and humiliated, wearing a hat and pushing a pram, married.

When I returned to Carlin Beck, it was to discover that my mother's importunities had prevailed with my father. Although the wage offered was smaller than that which he received in Carlin Beck, my father had applied for the Molethorpe job they had been discussing when I left. He was appointed, and the wage was raised to Carlin Beck level.

That was up the steep hill from Ellen Brig. Although it lay within the town limits of Hinderholme, the co-operative society was a small, independent one.

My father was much liked at the miners' end of Carlin Beck. We had electricity, and they wanted to put him on the town council as a Liberal. That was as near as he ever came to being a public figure. He now gave vent to as much bitterness as I ever heard him express before my mother.

He said:

'I hope you'll be suited this time, Ethel lass. I' two years I shall be forty-five. At forty-five you can't start a new job. They reckon you're too old.'

In later years, my mother would say to me:

'I held him back. I s' never forgive myself.'

My feelings were unmixed. I spent the remainder of the holidays and the first three weeks of the autumn term in a haze of contentment. On my last day at Carlin Beck Grammar School, I went to say good-bye to Mr Allendale, my father having said that I ought to. I was taken aback by the almost tearful warmth of the Boss's manner, as he wished me luck.

This time, my father was the last to move. The house was already got. It was in the same road as the Shop and had been occupied by the retiring drapery manager. In order that she might have it thoroughly scrubbed before the furniture arrived, my mother took Marjorie with her to stay at Holt End, leaving my sister with Grandad Sykes while she herself went to work on the new house during the day. I stayed with A'ntie Beulah, Uncle Nathan Haigh and Gertie in Bradford Road. I walked from there to the Grange, my scholarship having been re-transferred. Only when all was ready did my father come up with Mr Dadd and the furniture. We had been away from Hinderholme two years almost to the day.

THE CREMATORIUM LIES IN A PART OF LEEDS I HAD never before visited, out, I fancy, beyond the women's hostels and the playing fields. Odd that, in four years, I never went near the university playing fields, though part of the time I played football for Grange Old Boys.

Jenny Cowan was at the crematorium before us. She came to meet us as we got out of the car. I should have recognised her, quite unwarned. There she was, tall, fair-haired, handsome, in full mourning, very well-dressed, with a small, contented-looking, evidently prosperous new husband beside her, not so dark as Jack Greenlees.

The coffin was draped with a violet pall, silver-edged and bearing some design of a silver cross. A non-denominational person in an academic gown uttered large, non-denominational sentiments. As the coffin began to slide down the ramp, a gramophone record played *Abide With Me*. The gladioli went to local hospitals.

Anxious to be modern and please her children, my mother asked us afterwards if we thought one of those iron name-plates should be made and plugged into the lawn on which the ashes were scattered. No, Marjorie and I agreed, just let the ashes be scattered, with no memorial.

We drove back behind the top-hatted mutes. There was a luncheon, which had been ordered beforehand, at a restaurant in Hinderholme. As soon as we got back here, my mother changed out of her black frock.

My father is two or three handfuls of cooling ash, perhaps not yet scattered. I am head of the family. I am clan chief, the Atha of Ellen Brig, Pitt Rise and Welshport.

Both clan and inheritance are small. With the insurance, my mother will have about seven hundred pounds and the house. My patrimony will be a light overcoat of red tweed, a suit which fits me perfectly, an umbrella with engraved silver ring and a box of tools, less a diamond glass-cutter promised to the deaf young man next door.

The piano in the front room belongs to my sister, Mrs George Binns. I suppose it would be in order to play it now, so long as I didn't play anything too frivolous or too loud. A bit of Mendelssohn or a bit of Schumann perhaps or a Beethoven slow movement. It will have to be slow, because it will have to be easy. I haven't lived with a piano for years, at least not with a piano that I could bear.

It still is a very good piano. It cost twenty pounds before the Great War. A German make. Something like *Eichendorff*, but the gilt letters are worn away by fingernail-impact, mine for the most part. I gave up having lessons just before we moved to Carlin Beck. I didn't start again the year we returned. I hadn't minded. I might never have wanted to start again, but for Peter Holmes. I wonder. He was the occasion of my wanting, but it was only after I'd finished with him that the thing itself became really important to me. There would surely have been alternative occasions.

MARJORIE AND GEORGE HAVE GONE OUT FOR A WALK.
My mother went down the road and is sitting no doubt
somewhere inside the chapel I can see. That is where
Marjorie and George were married last year. Perhaps
I ought to go up to Linfootlock Wesleyans this evening
and see who is still there.

A bit to the right, starting two or three hundred
yards away, perhaps a quarter of a mile, the Scar rises
steeply out of Ellen Brig and up to Molethorpe, with
Cowl Hill beyond. A bit more than half way up, Tenpetty Row branches off to the right. If there is time this
afternoon, I shall walk that way and beyond Molethorpe and climb Cowl Hill and look across Hinderholme from above and to the south.

Halfway up the Scar, the gradient is as sharp as it is
on the sea front to the south of Gwaelod. Those houses
had to be built with two floors at the front and three
at the back. Then the back gardens had to be terraced.
The garden walls drop thirty or forty feet sheer to the
sloping field my father had to cross diagonally on his
way to work, once we had moved down here. The ten
outdoor privies spaced regularly along that stretch of

high wall are a landmark for the whole of Ellen Brig, and their crenellation may also be seen over the viaduct from Mallalieu Park, which I take to be in Linfootlock.

It was the steps which in the first place appalled my mother, though she was not then lame. Apart from the usual stairs between the front room and the bedrooms, there was a flight of stone steps from the front room down to the kitchen. Outside the kitchen door, there were four doorsteps to be scoured. The garden path was stepped, and the passage, which divided the row into two equal parts, contained a flight of steps, which she, together with the nine other householders, would have to take her turn to clean. But also, once more, we had no bathroom. Worst of all, we now became subject to weekly visits of the tub cart, a mark of distinct social retrogression. It was a mechanised tub cart. A horse could not have drawn a tub cart up the Scar. Even the mechanised one did not come straight up the hill from Ellen Brig, but took a devious route which brought it into the Scar halfway up, along the road where I turned off on my way to school.

Beyond the houses facing ours at the front (and thus further uphill, but the gradient slackened markedly at that point), my father rented a small field, which he turned into much-divided hen run, keeping, I suppose, about a hundred head of poultry, including ducks and geese. That was a bit of a lucky strike. My father had not wanted to come back, and by and large he did not like the people at the Shop in Molethorpe nearly so well as he had liked those at Carlin Beck.

I used the hen run. I soon killed my rabbits by over-feeding, but there were corners in that territory where

I could sit and read out of doors when I did not feel impelled to walk up Cowl Hill or over to Linfootlock, where most of my friends still were.

That was a walk of something over a mile, down the Scar into Ellen Brig, through Ellen Brig and up Ram Lane, bearing right by the engineering works (subsequently, of course, back down Ram Lane and up the very steep Scar). To and from school, I must have walked eight or nine miles a day, with sometimes a third trip to the Grange in the evening for a concert, or rehearsal for a concert, or a debate. There were only two Grange boys in that part of Molethorpe, and neither of them was in the same form as myself.

At school, I had to pronounce my Latin differently. As it was the only subject in which I was more advanced than third-year boys at the Grange and as my old-fashioned pronunciation concealed even this fact, I was put into Form III B. Living in Tenpetty Row inclined me to solitariness. Being in III B made me lazy at school. There was no competition in III B. The clever boys were elsewhere. After a year, I went into IV A.

I made no close friendships in III B, and the masters who taught us there have become unvivid in my mind, though I dare say I could name them all. I was not seriously discontented with my life. I had taken to reading widely. I would call in at the public libraries on my way home from school in the evening.

My reading tended strongly towards verse and more especially towards the Greeks in translation. No Greek was taught either at Carlin Beck or now at the Grange, but the first serious book I bought with my own money was the plays of Aeschylus in a World's Classics edition. Before long, I was stuck into the rows of Loeb Classics at the library.

There were also the weeklies, *John o' London's*, *T.P.'s*, *Everyman*, *The Outline*. *The Outline* was rather scientific and philosophical than literary. It led me to volumes of controversy between Hilaire Belloc and H. G. Wells, to Wells's *Outline of History* and to two volumes of philosophy from the Greeks to Herbert Spencer. These are still in the glass-fronted cupboard upstairs.

My father left school at the age of twelve. Since then, he boasted, he had not read a book. He used to tell me that I should go mad with reading. Yet he must have bought me those books and subscribed to the weeklies for me. Through the Shop, he was able to get books at wholesale price.

In an unguarded moment, he radically damaged the relations between himself and me on what might be called a philosophical point. This was while I was still in III B. In Physics, we had been doing theory of light. I was fascinated by the revelation of all that underlies so much of the philosophy I have read since.

It must have been in winter. One dinner-time, sitting in front of the fire during the few minutes before I needed to set off back to school and he to the Shop, I tried to share the interest with my father. I explained to him that the kettle was not really black or the flame orange, but that the impression was due to the manner in which these objects absorbed and reflected the light. My father told me briefly not to be silly.

He may have thought that I was showing off. He

144

may have thought that I had got it wrong. He may have been a prey to some private resentment at the time. However it may have been, the harm was done. I was deeply offended, and I decided that frank communication between us was hopeless. I should never again try to interest my father in any preoccupation of my own. The offence and the resolution stuck. Thereafter, I sometimes treated my father with inward disdain.

Things got worse afterwards, while I was at Leeds. On my side, feelings of guilt had come into play. I was not working enough. I did not mean to teach, as I had pretended I wanted to. I was cheating on my dinner money, going without lunch in the refectory in order to buy cigarettes. A shocking lack of candour had developed, and my father made one fumbling attempt to break it down, asking me what was 'the matter'. I brushed him off, though I think I would have preferred to explain if I could.

Yet he accepted my bad degree, which must have puzzled him, since he'd always supposed me bright. And, during my political phase the year after, there occurred one moment which even I, in my graceless state, was touched by.

My father was, if anything, a Liberal, as I suppose most people were in Hinderholme. The only political principle he admitted was that of voting 'for the best man', but it turned out in practice that the best man was always the Liberal candidate.

It was after we had moved into this house. Before going to bed, my father often thought beside the fire, while taking his boots off. He always sat in the chair in which he collapsed only last Monday.

K

He would let my mother go upstairs, then take one boot off and ease the toes of that foot with his fingers. A meditative stare would come into his pale-blue eyes and remain there for two, three or four minutes, after which he would sigh deeply, gnaw his now close-trimmed, greying moustache and take off the other boot. On that side of the fireplace, there is a small cupboard at ground level. From this my father would extract his slippers, push his toes into them and shuffle off to bed.

During my political phase, having got his slippers on but not yet having stood up, he one night addressed me.

'Look, Harold lad,' he said, 'have you been getting mixed up wi' t' communists?'

I agreed that you could call it that. No doubt I had left some pamphlet lying about, though I had also formed the impression that my letters were being opened in the post.

My father sat where he was for a moment longer, then sighed and stood up.

'Ay, well,' he said, 'if you get yourself into trouble don't expect me to come and bail you out, that's all. T' time's not ripe for that yet.'

And off he shuffled to bed. At that moment, I truly loved my father. But indeed I had never, as I should later discover to be almost common form among the young men I knew in London, 'hated' him. When I first heard of a young man hating his father, I thought what a very odd thing that was to do, though clearly a certain *chic* attached to it.

My mother is back from chapel. Since the joint is apparently cooking as it should and the vegetables are prepared, she has gone upstairs to change out of her mourning again. There is method in this. We are visiting A'ntie Ada this afternoon, and she is not to be informed of my father's death.

At the chapel, a young man has been testifying. What Jesus has saved him from, I didn't gather. No doubt this is something left over from a revival, like the one at Linfootlock sixteen years ago. That was a matter of months before I started my political phase. There was some connection, I dare say.

There were two appalling students from some theological college. In dreadful, bleating, sibilant voices, they sang childish words set to waltz tunes. The whole congregation sweated with embarrassment. Then they began to call out to us, imploring us to come and cast ourselves down at the communion rail and give ourselves to Jesus. This left us three alternatives.

You could leave the chapel. That would have seemed unsociable. Besides, you might be missing something. You could sit in your place, with a set and unsympathetic face, while, one after another, the faces of people you knew turned red and decomposed into tears. Then they got up and went to the altar rail, either straight forward or, if they were in the gallery or the choir, out by the nearest door and down the steps to reappear below. Or you could go down and give yourself to Jesus.

There was a further complication. You had an agreement beforehand with two other Leeds commuters, who both sang in the choir. If one of us went down, the others would join him. This was to be a form of amusement.

For that evening was the climax of a week's revival. There had been smaller meetings at the Wesley Guild, the Men's Bible Class, the Rechabites and so on. At those already, several people we knew were reported as having stood up in tears, confessed to a fondness for the bottle or something of the kind and been washed in the blood of the Lamb. One of the two undergraduates in the choir, a gas engineer, a humorist and a sceptic, had been the first to go down. By the expression on his face, his intention had been serious. Not long after, the physicist had gone down.

By the time I reached the communion rail, there was a crowd kneeling there. As yet others joined us, it became a struggling, suffocating heap.

On either side of me, nice-looking girls in their Sunday clothes, hot and sweet-smelling, wept, snuffled and shook. I was somewhere near Mildred Walsh and her sister Connie. Their father, a plump insurance man in black coat and striped trousers, with other dignitaries of the chapel who had found Jesus long ago, walked up and down behind us, gulping and stroking our heads and shoulders and saying in broken voices how glad they were that we had been saved.

Eventually, the female sheep were separated from the male goats. The sheep went into the minister's vestry with the little, red-haired student who looked like a reformed cracksman. The goats went into the choir vestry. The tall, pimply student with dark, plastered hair talked confidentially to us, the men. The witness he bore on his own account was that Jesus had formerly saved him from the sin of self-abuse.

The gas engineer and the physicist were in earnest.

Afterwards, I had to go round with them to the house where the circuit minister lived, at that time a big, over-emotional, old-womanly Scot, himself much given to kneeling down in the pulpit and, while somebody in the congregation led us in prayer, shouting out, 'Hallelujah!' and 'Selah!' and 'Praise the Lord!' The gas engineer and the physicist wanted to preach and testify.

They did preach and testify, in that and other chapels. I did not attend their services. In fact, I stopped going to chapel altogether. I shan't, I think, go up to Linfootlock this evening.

THE BRILLIANT SUNLIGHT AT THESE TALL WINDOWS mercilessly displays A'ntie Ada's sallow, blotched face, paralysed down one side, talking desperately in words I cannot follow at all, though Marjorie seems able to make them out. So, to some extent, do my mother and Uncle Arthur. I smile. Every now and then, I murmur sagaciously, as though it were all perfectly intelligible to me and very interesting, but there is not even facial expression to guide me as to whether at any given moment a yes or a no is expected of me. A'ntie Ada looks wildly agitated, but the imposed contortion of her features may account for that. I do not gather from my sister's asides that the discourse itself is anguished or even particularly urgent. The red blotches are, I seem to remember hearing (perhaps from Kenneth Fain-wright), one of the normal accompaniments of a stroke.

I heard my mother say:

'Alfred couldn't come. . . .'

But in the general babble I didn't gather whether my father's absence was accounted for in detail. It would seem odd. He never did have occasions of his own on a Sunday afternoon. He ought to have been here.

I also don't know whether A'ntie Ada is still indignant with her elder sister for sending her to the Workhouse. If she has managed to understand anything of what the nurses or the women in the neighbouring beds have said to her, perhaps by now she knows that this is no longer the Workhouse. Indeed, this building never was part of the Workhouse. We approached it by way of what was never a Workhouse entrance, near the bottom end of Mallalieu Park.

As a child, I thought A'ntie Ada fat. She wasn't. This woman, now perhaps fatally stricken, was a big, handsome Juno. Quick-tempered, intermittently sulky, she carried herself proudly, and, when she bothered about her clothes, she dressed well, even after her marriage to the comically insignificant man standing between Marjorie and my mother.

At the time of her marriage, she would be in her late thirties. That was fourteen years after the birth of Cousin Roy, nine after his death. The footballer must have appeared when she was twenty-two or twenty-three. Even now, she will be less than sixty.

There were certainly other suitors between the footballer and Arthur Quarmby. During my last few years at home, A'ntie Ada and I were pretty thick, and she told me a good many intimate stories, including some about the senior History master at school, a big, shambling man. When Uncle Arthur appeared on the scene, nobody thought well of him. A'ntie Ada herself said that she knew everybody laughed at him, but that he was always very good to her.

He worked at a grocer's, Lipton's or the Maypole. He suffered with his feet. He blamed the cold concrete floors on which he served gods of bacon and butter, but in the Great War he'd marched hundreds of miles in the infantry. Talking about the war was one of his faults in the eyes of other people. He'd liked the War, whether it was a matter of queueing up outside brothels or being sent out sniping with telescopic sights. In general, he was considered to lack dignity.

It was just before we moved to Carlin Beck that he first appeared. A year after we'd returned to Hinderholme, the house at Holt End was dominated by the gaunt figure of Grandad Sykes dying upstairs. There he lay, a yellow-integumented skeleton, his short, dark hair, burning eyes and Kitchener moustache seeming to be military decorations brought out of a drawer to grace what was not yet a recognised death-bed. The only thing I knew about his illness was that he could not eat. They tried feeding him through a tube, but he would not have it. It was a slow death, and until it took place there was no question of Arthur Quarmby marrying into the family.

At Bradford Road, Gordon Broadbent had not yet come to the point of marrying Gertie, when we returned from Carlin Beck or a year after that. Then, in early 1927, it began to be understood that they would be getting married in the summer.

'It's about time,' said A'ntie Beulah. 'They've been courting a lot too long. It isn't fair to Gertie.'

That would be just before Easter. I was in IV A then.

In June, I should be taking Matriculation. I was fifteen. I was in love with Peter Holmes.

A bell rings in the ward. Visitors standing about the other beds, one or two of those who have come alone sitting, begin to move away. We have been here, I suppose, for twenty minutes. During that time, A'ntie Ada's twisted face, with its livid blotches, has not stopped, as it seems, expostulating. We have nodded, smiled, looked grave, murmured. I have not understood a single word.

It was difficult to feel anything but embarrassment and a hope that the trouble will soon be resolved, one way or another. And yet I suppose I was much attached to A'ntie Ada. In a sort of way, I suppose I liked Uncle Arthur Quarmby, too. Certainly, I went up to Holt End pretty often in later years. I found those two easy. I talked to A'ntie Ada about my girls. I did not talk to her about Peter Holmes. Still, in his time I did not often go up to Holt End. It is hard not to be treacherous to the dying. I did not like the smell in the room where Grandad Sykes lay crater-eyed, with yellow, skeleton arm on the quilt.

Now we are on the broad concrete path which descends to the entrance by Mallalieu Park bottom gates. The way lies downhill as far as Ellen Brig and then fifty yards up Ram Lane before we turn off. With her stick and with the iron bored through the heel of her shoe and strapped about her thin shank, my mother bobs a little but moves at a good speed. I walk on her left, my tall sister on her right. Beyond my sister, with bowler hat, bright boots and stick, Arthur, proceeding gingerly on his bad feet, has started crying. We all pretend not to notice. He will have pulled himself together before we get back to the house.

AT SPEECH DAY IN THE TOWN HALL, THE BOY IN A lower form who lived near us in Molethorpe would be called upon for cascades of Liszt or Mendelssohn. Peter had been just adequate enough to represent last year's III A at a school concert at the end of the summer term. He had played *In a Monastery Garden* by Albert W. Ketèlbey. On that occasion, it was the music which had interested me. I got my mother to buy me *In a Monastery Garden* and another piece by the same composer, *Chal Romano*. These were added to the small list of my mother's favourite pieces, the Barcarolle from *The Tales of Hoffman*, a characteristic gavotte called *Rendezvous*, the currently popular Heykens *Serenade*, the Beethoven Minuet in G recently made into a song called *Mignonette*, *The Blue Danube* and what was simply known as Rachmaninov's *Prelude*. All through the years during which I had not been receiving piano lessons, I had now and then been bribed or cajoled into playing for her as much as I could still manage of these trifles and of the piano arrangements of such overtures as *Zampa* and *Poet and Peasant*.

At the Christmas concert in IV A, what Peter Holmes played was the 'Caprice de Nanette' from the *Petite Suite de Concert* by Coleridge-Taylor. He lived in the main road to the right of Ellen Brig from here. I can see the house. At any rate, I could a moment ago. A slight heat-haze seems to be developing into a late-afternoon ground mist over all the low-lying parts of the town. He lived with a widowed mother and sang in a church choir. I can see the church steeple. That, too, lies to the townward side of Ellen Brig.

Statistically, it seems probable that in any large class of boys there will always be one or two who turn out sexually inverted. At the age of fifteen, they are not easily picked out. In fact, it is probably not yet certain which they will be. Some of their voices are broken, some not. Some complexions are smooth and dazzling, others muddy, on fire with pimples or in need of a shave. There are quiet and studious boys, others inclined to nothing but wild horseplay. Some blush at the very mention of certain matters, while others riot in obscenity and may claim, perhaps even truthfully, to have experienced full-scale sex already. The decisive experiences are still likely enough to lie in the future. According to Kenneth Fainwright, to be the son of a widow already constitutes a predisposition.

Peter Holmes was quiet, petal-skinned, unbroken-voiced, not good at games, lacking in physical boldness. His hair was almost as fair as Mildred Walsh's, parted near the middle. His large, pale, grey-blue eyes, if they did not exactly protrude, yet lay very much *à fleur de tête*, as our French master, a briskly gesticulating Welsh-man, did not fail to point out by way of exemplifying the idiom. He was smaller than the average, and it was perhaps some breadth of pelvis which made him seem, among boys, a bit knock-kneed. His features, though rather aquiline, were delicate, his complexion opaque and creamy, sometimes with a high flush over the cheekbones. His fingers were thin, his hands fiddler's rather than pianist's hands.

He was thought a bit girlish. His performances on the football field and in the gymnasium were mildly ridiculed. But he was never persecuted or openly declared a nancy-boy, like Bertie Bower. Bertie was a screaming blond and very aggressive. Everybody knocked him about. Not that he always came off worst, by any means. He was both agile and unscrupulous and did not hesitate to sink his big white teeth in a hand or knee. For most of us, until the Easter of 1927, and some thereafter, including Peter Holmes, still wore short trousers at school, though most of us (but not Peter) wore our first long-trousered suits on Sundays.

Bertie Bower and Peter Holmes were friends in the sense that, as they were neighbours, they commonly walked and trammed home together. I think Bertie sang in the same church choir. I think his mother also was a widow. Of all the boys in IV A, he might have seemed the likeliest to turn out actively homosexual, though I did later hear tales to the contrary.

I don't know where Peter lives now or even what he does for a living. He may be the father of a large family. There is only one later counter-indication, and that is sound evidence only if I am right about the Law Barraclough set-up and Gordon Broadbent.

About George Milner I feel no doubt. Sheer arrogance of personality would lead him to open competition over girls, whatever contrary impulses may then have been summarily covered. Yet it was his attitude to Peter Holmes which upset me. His manner was at once teasing and chivalrous. He would put his arm about Peter's shoulders. This, I found, annoyed me. I did not at first recognise the feeling as jealousy.

The first unmistakable stab of love came in the gymnasium. Peter was hanging helplessly from the wall-bars, quite unable either to bend his arms or to raise his legs. The gym-master, the usual type of thick-set, bald, time-expired sergeant with big moustache and white sweater, was giving him individual attention. The touch of scarlet on Peter Holmes's cheekbones had spread over neck and ears. His big, luminous eyes seemed about to burst out of their sockets, like those of the fallen horse in Radcliffe Road back street or those of the conquered savages across whose necks their enemies launch a heavy canoe in *Coral Island*.

In the corridor at the end of the lesson, it was I who put my arm about his shoulders.

'You look hot, Holmesy,' I said, and touched his burning cheek with electrical finger. He smelled deliciously of his mother's scented soap.

Shortly thereafter, he and I went together to a lecture-with-gramophone-records on Beethoven's violin concerto by a local musicologist with a national reputation. And so it began with music. But it was Plato who made it clear that friendship could be given the name of love. The operative dialogue was *Lysis*, which, among those pale-green volumes, was bound up with *The Symposium* and *Gorgias*.

Hippothales' friend, Ctesippus, teased him with writing poems to Lysis, yet neither he nor Socrates thought being in love with a boy anything out of the ordinary. They were on their way 'by the road outside the town wall' from the Academy to a wrestling-school.

156

Hippothales had a rival, the showy Menexenus, whose uninhibited flattery had engaged the enchanting but foolish Lysis' interest, while Hippothales remained tongue-tied by his more serious passion. Socrates undertook to put all to rights by a discussion which should expose the superficiality of Menexenus's feelings.

In my own mind, I cast as Socrates our amiable, elderly Latin master. Not that he was ever involved in the matter, even by verbal comment of a satirical kind, though it was in his lessons that I normally sat by Peter Holmes and let my hand rest on a warm, smooth knee. The Latin master would, I felt sure, have understood. The ancient world seemed more real to him than the world of that day, and certainly he was a bachelor. George Milner, of course, was Menexenus. His temperamental arrogance came in part from the fact that his parents lived in the smartest part of Hinderholme. By the standards of most of us, he was a rich man's son. The figure conspicuously lacking was any Ctesippus.

There was a scene of jealousy at the chess-club after school on a Monday. Peter had taught me the moves, and halfway through a game George Milner came in and engaged him in conversation about a party he'd invited Peter to. I made my move, and Peter paid no attention. I picked up my satchel and stamped off, followed by a protesting cry from Peter and George Milner's laughter.

One hot Saturday afternoon, not long before Easter, Peter Holmes walked up the Scar. I met him by the Armageddon hut. We came up here, through Molethorpe proper and by a winding country lane to Cowl Hill and over Cowl Hill to the lane which now lies two or three hundred yards behind and below me. That was really country. There were farms. I suppose there still are. There were also woods, with bluebells and a stream.

In the lane, there was love-talk. This took the form of me asking Peter what he thought the most important thing in life. He hesitated. I suggested he answer in Latin. He said that it was *amicitia*. I said that it was *amor*. I can't remember whether this declaration was followed by some embrace or even a kiss.

I suppose I must have kissed Peter Holmes. I don't remember doing it, and one thing I find about memory is that, given some associated face or name, I remember all the kisses in my life, let alone the more intimate occasions, even when, as with Blod, these must by now approach four figures, a glorious addition sum which tomorrow, please Heaven, will be taken at least one more step towards its grand total (of course, memory needs more stimulus than face or name there, though it is strange even there what diverse occasions mere face or name will conjure up). Perhaps I didn't kiss Peter Holmes. Perhaps I merely nuzzled his face and avoided his mouth.

Certainly, we lay embraced, not, I think, in the woods beyond and below, but certainly in those beyond Mallalieu Park. Indeed, I remember once rising to my feet and searching the area about us because I had heard some crackling of twigs or bracken, as if there had been some peeping Tom around. In all those areas in which Hinderholme people notoriously made *al fresco* love, there was assumed to be a peeping Tom. It almost seemed as though peeping Toms were attached to such areas in a semi-official capacity. On the other hand, they were assumed to have put themselves so far outside the law that, if, for instance, you kicked a peeping Tom to death, no judge or magistrate would convict.

At Easter, there was to be a school trip to St. Pol de Léon in Britanny. I persuaded my father that to go on this would ensure me a good result in French in the examinations in June. By that time, however, the list was made up. By way of consolation, it was arranged that Peter Holmes and I should spend a week together at the Cowans' in Carlin Beck.

This would mean sharing a bed. In this prospect, I foresaw delightful, though somewhat indistinct, possibilities of a closer intimacy. Then another boy cancelled his booking for the Britanny trip, and my name was on the list. The fact may have saved both Peter Holmes and myself from a fate doubly worse than death. I don't know. Brittany without Peter seemed more alluring than a shared bed with. We might still go to Carlin Beck at Whitsuntide.

According to the text-books and Kenneth Fainwright, a homosexual phase normally precedes any interest in the opposite sex. It was not so in my case. At least until the point at which some form of 'crystallisation' had taken place about him, I would far rather my hand had rested on bare flesh above Mildred Walsh's knee, but no opportunity of experiencing this delight presented itself.

I did not in fact let my imagination play so much about Mildred as about her elder sister, Connie, a rosy, big-bosomed girl whose reputation was somewhat blown on, because she had been observed to go out driving with the son of the head of the engineering works, at which she worked as a clerk or secretary. In my head, Connie Walsh had more than once invitingly taken off all or most of her clothes. The likelihood of her doing so in reality seemed extremely remote. Clearly, such blissful revelations and their barely imaginable consequences must take place sometimes, perhaps in London or among the rich, but, for a start, it did not seem probable that any young woman as beautiful as Connie Walsh and as willing as she was reputed to be should ever be found alone in a house with me. Peter was at least accessible, and he had much of the charm and gentleness of a girl. There were *prima facie* difficulties in the way of any imagined consummation, but that fact had not seemed to bother Hippothales.

Temperamentally speaking, it was as a girl that I treated Peter Holmes. My attitude was protective and chivalrous. I remember how, on a Sunday afternoon walk, we compared hands. I felt, I dare say, all the more masculine for wearing long trousers as by then I did on Sundays, whereas he still wore short ones even on Sundays. My own hand, though neither coarse nor ill-formed, looked strong and square. The sight of his thin and delicate fingers beside it melted me to the core. I crushed his fingers in mine, and it did something to our breathing.

That was in the road near the far end of Mallalieu Park, where the rich men's houses and bungalows had grown up, including Law Barraclough's. There had seemed to be nobody else about, but, as we walked on, my arm about Peter's shoulders, his, I suppose, since he was shorter, at my waist, there was some one in a garden behind the tall hedge of one of the houses. We drew apart.

A man's voice said:

'Nay, yo' carry on, lads. That's the stuff. Young love, I always say.'

That was Law Barraclough's house. The man was Law Barraclough. Peter Holmes and I quickened our pace.

At that time, I don't think I'd heard any of the tales about Law Barraclough. I knew he'd become a director of Hinderholme United F.A.C., which made him quite a figure in the town. Uncle Nathan Haigh didn't seem to like him, but that might have been on political grounds.

I could not have said exactly what it was in his words that I found so objectionable, but in his tone there was something which obscurely shamed me. Neither Peter nor I made any comment on what, after all, had been words of friendly reassurance and encouragement spoken without intended concealment through his own hedge by a man on his own lawn, provoked by our embarrassed drawing apart. But I must not give too much weight to this incident. At the time, I attached very little to it.

At Easter, the party from school crossed by night from Southampton and saw St. Malo born of the morning light. We briefly studied the town and moved on by train to St. Pol de Léon, which we reached in the afternoon and settled ourselves in the annexe of a hotel. In the streets, a local citizen entered into conversation with us. He was rather drunk and spoke English fluently with a Scotch accent.

The master in charge of the party was Major Blunt, who was fairly new to the school but by no means one of the lesser brethren. He somewhat resembled the Boss at Carlin Beck even in his physical appearance. He was bald, grew a very small ginger moustache, supported a heavy body on thin legs, a fact the more apparent because he frequently wore plus fours even in school. He wore a monocle slung around his neck, but, as it never went up to his eye unless he really wanted to peer at something in small print, we did not hold this against him. On the whole, he was liked by the boys, though he embarrassed some of the masters by prefixing their names with war-time military ranks they, unlike himself, had shed in civilian life more than eight years before.

At the end of the evening meal, Major Blunt stood up and, raising his glass of wine, said:

'Gentlemen, the King!'

Sheepishly, we all stood up with our glasses of water and did as Major Blunt evidently meant us to. We thought it rather affected on Major Blunt's part, but perhaps it was an idea of his for impressing the natives.

Next day, the sun blazed, and we bathed on the beach at Pempoul, where we also drank grenadine, a drink, I felt, if anything more sophisticated than milk-and-soda. At the hotel, we drank coffee and ate omelettes which, I decided, were things I must get my mother to do at home.

We went out in fishing-boats and were astonished by the candour with which the skipper and his men made water over the gunwale. We took a train to Brest and looked at the ships. We continued to toast the King.

We bought *eau de Cologne* and ornamental *sabots* and sent postcards to our relatives and friends. We smoked Craven 'A' and *Gauloises 'Maryland'*. That was my introduction to smoking. Arthur Lumb and Freddie Fischer had smoked while I still lived in Radcliffe Road, but at that time I would not join them, having been convinced by the adult propaganda which said that it would stunt my growth.

On the return journey, we scattered for lunch in St. Malo. I had cider with my luncheon. I had friends in the party, but for some reason I had chosen to eat alone. We crossed that afternoon through sunlit spray and rounded the Needles by twilight. At Hinderholme, my father met the train. He told me not to be surprised, when I got home, to see my mother in black. Grandad Sykes had died while I was away, and the funeral had taken place only the day before.

It must have been difficult to determine the precise moment at which, or even the day on which, Grandad Sykes died. I felt a grief which I quickly repressed. The practical difference this death was going to make was that Uncle Arthur could now marry A'ntie Ada and live in that house.

The afternoon of the following day, I met Peter Holmes by the Armageddon hut, and we came up here. Among these ancient British earthworks, there were (there are) many hollows in the ground. We settled in one of them, sheltered from the light wind, I suppose not more than fifty yards from where I now stand. I cannot guess at the particular patch of parched grass on which, after puffing for a while at a 'Maryland' cigarette, Peter was sick. I told him about all that gorse, on islands out to sea and all along the mainland as seen from boats. I described a village wedding on which we had stumbled by chance, on entering a church to look at the historical remains. But he was puking. That was the end of the affair.

The school holidays were not yet over. On Friday afternoon I went down to the covered market in town. This was a place to which I had formerly been taken, sometimes unwillingly, by my mother, on Saturdays, on our way to Holt End. I had begun to frequent it myself for two main reasons. On the upper floor of the market, there were two second-hand bookstalls. Among the shops in the narrow street along its north side were two music shops, which sold music in editions cheaper than the Augener, Langnick, Schirmer and Bosworth editions normally stocked by the music shops in Kirkgate.

On that particular Friday, I went to the covered market for quite a different reason. On my last visits, before Easter, I had noticed, serving at one of the sweet stalls, a handsome, dark-eyed, Eton-cropped girl in a mauve overall, whose legs were as ornamental as ever I had thought Mildred Walsh's and whose bold manner I admired. That Friday afternoon, I bought a quarter of boiled sweets from her and, with my twopence, gave her a note suggesting that we meet and stating that I would come for a further quarter of sweets at the same time the following day, when I hoped to receive her reply.

On Saturday afternoon, she gave me no sign of recognition, and neither with nor inside my bag of sweets was there any note stating date and time. On

Monday, we returned to school. I returned in long trousers, having, like any respectable person, begun wearing a new suit on Easter Sunday. Peter Holmes was still in short trousers. In the evening, I posted him at the entrance to the closed market nearest to the mauve girl's sweet stall, with instructions to wait until the market closed, to follow the girl home and to report to me next day on where she lived. I left him there and went home to my tea. For his failure, next day, to provide me with any useful information, I never forgave him.

For that and for being sick in front of me. There was no renewed talk of our going to Carlin Beck together at Whitsuntide. I did not go to Carlin Beck that year. The place itself held little attraction for me. My parents and Marjorie were going to take their summer holidays there, leaving me at home by myself.

I must go carefully now about the order in which things happened. I suppose that it would be at Whitsuntide when A'ntie Ada and Arthur Quarmby got married and went on their honeymoon to Whitley Bay.

Before that, at some trades exhibition in the Town Hall, my mother had bought a cylindrical contraption to whip up the whites of eggs and make what I should now call an *omelette soufflée*. I also made coffee straight in the cup. My father viewed the proceeding with disfavour. He now darkly said not only that I should go mad with reading but also that I should turn brown with drinking coffee. He was also inclined to fear that I had been unsettled by foreign travel.

In June, I sat for my examinations. Towards the end of the month, a total eclipse of the early morning sun was theoretically visible in England and more especially in Yorkshire. Matriculation was not quite over, but we had no papers that day, and so there was a holiday from school. I meant to climb up here to the top of Cowl Hill before breakfast. I had smoked a piece of glass the night before.

My mother did not call me quite soon enough. I could not be absolutely certain of reaching the great local vantage-point in time. I was, I dare say, half glad of the excuse. I lay in bed and watched the light through the curtains increase and then fade again. I got up and drew the curtains upon a dark world.

In Tenpetty Row, my room, at the back of the house, faced more or less due north. The view from its windows was a wide one, though the moorland beyond Linfootlock, on the horizon, with the silhouetted cranes of its quarries, is, I would say, higher than that part of Molethorpe. Certainly, though in the distance it looks a bit hazy now, the rising white mist has not reached it yet by a long way. The mist is a milky sea in the two-fold valley and rises halfway up the vertical columns of the viaduct across the Helm. That morning, the play of light over the land was curious enough, its rapid changes of intensity dramatic.

I heard afterwards that the eclipse had never been very clearly visible. There had been cloud and drizzle until it was almost over. If I had come up here, I should have had to move over to the right. The sun would have risen over the lower ground towards Wakefield, through which the Helm and Hinder flow conjoined.

In the kitchen downstairs, the table stood under the

window. My place for meals was at the end nearest the door. In summer, we ate with the door open. If I drew my chair back a little and turned my head to the right, the view would be much the same as from my bedroom window. I saw the same cranes traced upon the skyline. If I got up from the table, I saw the viaduct to the left, with the trees of Mallalieu Park visible above it and through its arches.

When I was sitting at table, the wireless stood on a bracket over my head. At dinner-time on Fridays, a man called Christopher Stone played new gramophone records. At a guess, it was in early July that year that he played a new recording of the Prelude to Wagner's *Tristan und Isolde*. I had not heard it before, and this yearning chromaticism affected me as I had not before been affected by music. At the sixth bar, my scalp began to tingle. I thought I should have fainted.

I thought that I might compose music. I had previously thought I might be a poet. I supposed one might contrive to be both, writing poems and then turning them into songs and choral works and operas. I must certainly take up the piano again. It was almost five years since I'd had lessons. I could never reach competition standard now, but still might learn to play Beethoven, Chopin and Liszt. At the public library, there were books *about* music, text-books of harmony and counterpoint with exercises I could do by myself, books analysing the great works, showing how they were made.

There was no chance whatever of my father letting me go to the Royal College of Music in London. He might let me go to a university. Other boys in IV A were expecting to go to a university, 'Bee' Webb for one. Several boys in the Sixth would be going to Oxford that autumn.

If I went to a university, I supposed that would mean I should have to be a teacher. Perhaps I could go to Oxford for a while and then leave it like Matthew Arnold's scholar gipsy and be a mysterious, wandering poet or musician or both.

Well, of course, I have turned out to be neither. I publish other people's books, and I contrive a little foreign travel in these days of currency restriction by writing informative or impressionistic articles from abroad. I have written no verse and no music since the war. Still, I did once try my hand at intransigence. I hope yet to publish another book of my own, though no doubt it will be in prose. There are two children to be fed and clothed. And those were my reflections twenty-one years ago. I saw myself as not yet a dedicated spirit, but as one to whom dedication was possible.

Then, about the middle of July, a fortnight before my sixteenth birthday, there was advertised among the Situations Vacant in a Monday evening's *Hinderholme Guardian* a junior clerk's job at the Town Hall. The advertisement caught my father's eye. That I should work in the Town Hall represented the height of my father's ambition. I must apply for the job.

The Matriculation results were not yet out, I said. My father perceived the relevance of that fact, but had no doubt that the Town Clerk was also aware of it.

I must write to Mr Allendale at Carlin Beck, and to-morrow I must ask the headmaster at the Grange for a testimonial. My father studied my discontented air and expressed once more his fear that I had been unsettled by foreign travel.

My Grange testimonial credited me with common sense, initiative and a mind of my own. The Boss's was even better. I've seen it, I think, in the glass-fronted cupboard at home. I must read it again when I get back.

My father had said more than once:

'He's a nice man, is Mr Allendale.'

Yes, he was a nice man. It is moving to think that he still remembered me so kindly at that point in his own life. At the time, I was moved only to wish that he had not remembered me at all or had thought ill of me, for what he wrote made the danger of a dreadful job at the Town Hall only more real. I hoped bad handwriting might stand me in good stead, but my father made me write out the application again.

A letter arrived, requiring me to present myself on a Friday afternoon at the Town Hall. I was trapped.

On Thursday evening, I went up to Holt End. I smoked Uncle Arthur's Woodbines, ate fish and chips from the shop next door and drank coffee, of which A'ntie Ada had bought a special tin to gratify my unnatural craving for the beverage. There was a new suite and a wireless set in that room, and Woodbines, to say nothing of coffee, had begun to drive out the smell of poverty.

Matthew Arnold had been a set book for Matriculation. If only for that reason, he had become the first important poet in my life, preceding even Keats. I knew a lot of Matthew Arnold by heart. As I walked home through town, it was not so much *The Scholar*

Gipsy I had in mind as another poem called *A Summer Night*.

> In the deserted moon-blanch'd street
> How lonely rings the echo of my feet!
> Those windows, which I gaze at, frown,
> Silent and white, unopening down,
> Repellent as the world:—but see!
> A break between the housetops shows
> The moon, and, lost behind her, fading dim
> Into the dewy dark obscurity
> Doth a whole tract of heaven disclose. . . .

A break in the housetops came after the Model Lodging House in Folly Hill. Against a tract of heaven, I saw the hill on which I now stand, its watch-tower sharply silhouetted, a moon near full riding over the hill. A tram clanged down Folly Hill, braking hard and emitting blue flashes.

It was at Folly Brig that, thirteen years later, my mother would lie in the black-out, knocked down by the swinging trailer of an R.A.F. lorry, till hands uninstructed on the subject of compound fractures dragged her into the shop nearby. I had no premonition of that. I thought only of how my own life was taking a direction I had not chosen.

> . . . And I, I know not if to pray
> Still to be what I am, or yield, and be
> Like all the other men I see.
>   For most men in a brazen prison live,
> Where in the sun's hot eye,
> With heads bent o'er their toil, they languidly
> Their lives to some unmeaning taskwork give,

Dreaming of naught beyond their prison wall.
And as, year after year,
Fresh products of their barren labour fall,
From their tired hands, and rest
Never yet comes more near,
Gloom settles slowly down over their breast.
And while they try to stem
The waves of mournful thought by which they
    are prest,
Death in their prison reaches them
Unfreed, having seen nothing, still unblest.
    And the rest, a few,
Escape their prison, and depart . . .

I had no alternative plan. For the moment, all I needed was a reprieve, two years more at school, perhaps then a university. The important thing was, in the first place, not to get that Town Hall job to-morrow.

When I got home, I washed my hair. In the morning, I put no brilliantine on it, so that it fluffed up and made me look like an idiot. I put on a tight collar, which heightened the impression by shortening my neck and rounding my face. At the interview, I answered like an idiot, speaking inaudibly, pretending not to understand the questions, looking vaguely out of the window. I did not get the job.

My parents were off to stay with the Cowans in Carlin Beck. I was to stay at the house in Tenpetty Row by myself. I should make my own breakfast, tea and supper, and at dinner-time I could go down to A'ntie Beulah's. It seemed fair enough. I'd had my trip to Brittany at Easter, and I was not attracted by

Carlin Beck. In any case, somebody had to look after my father's poultry, which at that time included a large number of goslings. These were delicate. Each morning, a few of them would be found dead and had to be buried promptly in view of the hot weather.

Uncle Nathan's Gertie and Gordon Broadbent had found a house just off Bradford Road and were to be married on the Saturday before the August bank holiday. I don't remember my parents going to the wedding. I fancy they must have been to Carlin Beck for a fortnight and that Gertie and Gordon, going on their honeymoon to Southport for only a week, were married some days after my parents' departure.

And so it would be on the last Wednesday or Thursday in July when, during the course of an evening walk round Mallalieu Park, I saw my proleptic Uncle Gordon come out of Law Barraclough's front gate.

I was a bit surprised. I had not supposed the two knew each other. On the other hand, Uncle Gordon knew most of the United footballers, and Law Barraclough was a director. No doubt Uncle Gordon had called round to discuss some United matter. I had not supposed that he stood high in the counsels of Hinderholme United, but then I could not imagine him standing high in any counsels. Perhaps I underestimated him.

There was nothing which struck me as unusual in his manner. The impression Gordon Broadbent normally made was one of awkwardness and stupidity. I took him to be an exceptionally *stupid* man, though only moderately foolish. He was not, that is to say, as *silly* as Uncle Arthur, but I took him to be less intelligent, less quick-minded. I could not imagine him ever having got a sum right at school. Behind that deeply corrugated forehead, I could not imagine that anything went on whatever. His manner was always constrained, with the constraint of a man who has nothing to say and who accepts the fact that his opinion will not be sought.

I had never disliked him. On the other hand, I had never warmed positively towards him, as I did to Gertie, who was herself warm-hearted, responsive and gay. That evening, Gordon's long-jawed, darkly blood-congested face was as I always remembered, except when at Christmas the jaw drooped in an excess of giggling amiability over his beer.

As usual, we exchanged a few commonplaces. He enquired after the health of my father and mother. I asked after Gertie, checked up on their honeymoon dates, hoped the new house was ready and that they liked it. I was told that, of course, I must come round and see it as soon as they were settled in.

Uncle Gordon said:

'We never see you at the United now, Harold.'

'No. . . .'

A fortnight later, I should certainly wonder if I had given offence. The suspicion that I just might have was, I dare say, in my mind that evening a few minutes after we had separated at the corner. I had taken it that talk of the United was somehow coupled with the invitation to go and see the new Mr and Mrs G. Broadbent at their new house.

I nevertheless added:

' . . . No, I'm not very interested in footballers now.'

To say the least, that was priggish and uncalled-for and not at all likely to please a lifelong football enthusiast. If I thought of the matter afterwards that evening, I probably concluded that, since behind that furrowed brow was pure bone, small discourtesies would not penetrate. Uncle Gordon Broadbent would hardly be a touchy man or quick to take offence. My *manner* had been entirely amiable.

My parents and Marjorie went off to Carlin Beck. The sun blazed. I ate bread and jam, dipped bread in bacon fat, occasionally worked the omelette machine, drank more coffee than tea. At first I went down to A'ntie Beulah's for my dinner, but grew a bit tired of the long journey by tram and A'ntie Beulah's sometimes excessive solicitousness. Then, for a day or two, I spent at dinner-time the money I had been given for fish-and-chips in the evening. I got from the library books on harmony and counterpoint by Ebenezer Prout. I mixed the hens' mash, saw that they had plenty of water and grit. I had the wireless to myself and could listen uninhibited by my mother to things like Schoenberg's *Gurrelieder* and a play by a modern poet called Ezra Pound about Villon and some others being hanged, the gibbets creaking eerily in the wind.

Sometimes, I studied Prout in the front room upstairs, sitting on the music stool made by my father and latterly bulging with music, the book propped up on the music stand, hands free to pick out the sequences of chords. Sometimes I read in the field, surrounded by poultry. Then I took against the place. The goslings were beginning to die faster. I left some too long unburied, and there was soon a stench and a crawling of grubs in the hot sun. This was soon quelled, but the impression remained.

No doubt it was to escape that impression that I climbed up here on the morning of the day, a Monday, on which my parents were due back, though it would be evening before they arrived. That day, there was a morning mist lingering over the low ground, though nothing like this present lactic sea, out of which tall chimneys, none of them visibly smoking, rise like dreaming spires, better, I'd say, than those of Oxford from any angle and in any light I've seen them.

That day, I decided I'd better go down to Bradford Road for my dinner. My parents would ask what I'd done. They would be discontented if I couldn't give the impression of having been down to A'ntie Beulah's most days. It would strike them as a negative abuse of hospitality.

I went down, as now I must do, and caught a tram in Molethorpe proper, which meant changing trams in town. The white mist now washes under the arches of the viaduct. The town is wholly concealed. I see only the tops of a few mill-chimneys standing on high ground, and even those are streaked with mist.

Gertie and Uncle Gordon were back from Southport. I did not say anything to A'ntie Beulah about calling round to see them that very day. It did not occur to me to call round until I left A'ntie Beulah's at tea-time. I knew Gertie and Gordon were back. I knew that Gordon had work that week. For the present, Gertie was not going back to the mill.

There was no answer when I knocked at the front door. I walked round to the back. There was no answer when I knocked on the back door. I hesitated. Gertie ought to have been back from her shopping or whatever she was doing, to make her husband's tea. If he was not back yet, Gordon oughtn't to be long coming home from the mill. Certainly, I'd heard a nearby buzzer some time ago.

The back garden was very small, little more than the kind of yard (though without the high walls) they'd had in the streets at the miners' end of Carlin Beck. There was nothing much growing, and much of the space was taken up by a shed. Part of this had been partitioned off as a coal-house. The door of the remainder stood open. I fancied a key to the back door of the house might be left on a nail inside the shed door.

Except for a broken chair and a roll of oilcloth, the shed was empty. There were no gardening tools or woodwork tools, such as there would have been in any such shed at home. There was no key on a nail. If there had been, I dare say I shouldn't have felt I could use it to let myself into a house I hadn't yet been introduced to.

It was as I stepped out of the shed that I saw Uncle Gordon. So he *was* in and hadn't answered the door. He couldn't have been in the lavatory when I knocked, because the lavatory was out at the back. He might have been washing himself at the kitchen sink, but he wasn't stripped to the waist. I could tell that, although I saw only his face above the lace curtain which covered the lower part of the window. I smiled at him. He put his tongue out at me.

I thought this was a joke. Gordon Broadbent had never been particularly high spirited, but perhaps marriage and the holiday at Southport and the new house had worked changes in him. I laughed and pointed to the back door and moved towards it. He shook his head.

For a moment, he might not have realised it was me. He might have thought it was just some boy from nowhere trespassing in his shed. But then he wasn't deaf. He knew I'd knocked at the front door and then at the back. If I could see him through the window, he could see me out in the daylight. There was even a bit of sun.

I must have offended him by what I had said ten days ago about not being very interested in footballers any longer. He certainly didn't mean to let me in. He didn't shout at me, but clearly he was sending me away. In fact he seemed in a towering rage. He glared. His eyes almost popped with fury. His face was more darkly congested than ever. He shook his head angrily and then more slowly and decidedly from side to side.

Gertie must be on her way back now. I should probably meet her in the street, fat and laughingly flustered with her pale, dimpled cheeks and red hair, hurrying, loaded with shopping. I went round to the front, into the street. A 'towering' rage was just about it. Unless the kitchen floor was raised, Uncle Gordon had either been standing on tiptoe to look down at me over the curtain or standing on something very low or crouched on a chair or buffet, because he'd only seemed a few inches taller than usual.

I turned into the main road. I did not meet Gertie. I caught a tram that went right through to Ellen Brig. I walked up the Scar and turned into Tenpetty Row. My parents had just got home.

The mist is still whiter and denser, though up here

I stand in sunlight and, over to the left, can see named hills remote in the Pennines. The top of the viaduct is just visible, like a great pier or causeway over the sea. In the town, I suppose the mist won't look white. It will be dark, and people will be expecting it to rain.

THIS IS THE BOSS'S TESTIMONIAL, ON A SMALL SHEET OF private writing paper, pale grey, the printed heading in very small blue capitals.

THE SCHOOL HOUSE,
CARLIN BECK,
NORTH YORKSHIRE

I have much pleasure in certifying to the character & ability of H. S. G. Atha who was at this school for 2 years, & left because his father left the district. He is a boy of exceptional character & ability. His work was always well & conscientiously done. He is a steady, loyal & reliable boy who is worthy of a responsible position & can be trusted to do his duty & to do it well.

G. L. M. Allendale M.A.
Cantab.

July 18, 1927   Headmaster

That put me right in the Gunga Din class.

The date is that of Blod's birthday. I must ask her to-morrow night if she can remember what she was doing that day, nine years before I met her.

'He was a very nice man, was Mr Allendale,' said my father.

178

That was about three weeks later. The summer term wouldn't have ended when the Boss wrote my testimonial. There'd been just one long, creosoted shed. The woodwork room, known as the carpenter's shop, had been one end of it. The rest was taken up by the Armoury. It was the day after, or the day but one after, the end of term when, on a hot afternoon, the Rev. Mr Allendale went down from the school-house to the Armoury and shot himself with one of the cavalry carbines we'd used for drilling with in the O.T.C. The news had been fresh when Marjorie and my parents arrived to stay with the Cowans. It was said that the Boss had been gambling and that he had acquired large debts.

'He was a nice man,' said my father. 'I s' always remember him saying:

' "Nay, Mr Atha, if there isn't a place, we'll make one." '

His eyes were the least bit red, and he chewed his moustache with grief.

The Matriculation results were out. I had done well. I introduced the subject of universities. I said I wanted to teach.

'All right,' said my father. 'We'll go and see Mr Beaumont.'

A foreman engineer, Mr Beaumont had a son at the university, either Leeds or Manchester. Frank Beaumont was a big, fair, good looking young man. When we lived in Radcliffe Road, I had known him as the best-natured, friendliest of the older boys in the neighbourhood. The Beaumonts lived in the street which continued Radcliffe Road towards town, a sort of Lower

Radcliffe Road. Its backs looked out on the Wreck, where the silk-mill now stood.

It must have been the evening but one after my parents' return from Carlin Beck. This seems a bit unlikely in view of the fact that only that day had A'ntie Beulah telephoned to the Shop, while my father was serving a customer, to say that she wanted to see him at Bradford Road that evening. Perhaps she and Uncle Nathan Haigh were a day out in their reckoning of when my parents were due back. At any rate, my father was to go down to Bradford Road after our visit to Mr Beaumont's.

Frank Beaumont had stayed in. He was dressed in flannels and blazer. He was going out to play tennis at the Wesleyans, perhaps with Mildred and Connie Walsh, who both played well. He told my father what he wanted to know about scholarships, bursaries and so on. When he had gone out, my father asked Mr Beaumont whether Frank had ever given his parents reason to think that a university education had made him ashamed of them.

Mr Beaumont had suffered from the same disquietude. Indeed, there had been one terrible day when he was in town and saw Frank and some of his friends coming along towards him on the other side of the road. Frank hadn't let on. He hadn't called out, and he hadn't looked at his father.

However, the story had a happy ending. When Mr Beaumont spoke to Frank later about the incident, Frank had denied seeing his father, and Mr Beaumont had believed his son.

'He's not a deep one, Alfred,' said Mr Beaumont.

'I'd always know when he wasn't speaking the truth.'

My father looked sideways at me. Mr Beaumont ventured the opinion that he didn't reckon I was a deep one, either. Nor, it seemed, did I look as though I was one to be ashamed of my parents as a result of too much education.

I dare say I blushed gracefully. I wished I was out of that house.

We separated at the bottom of Radcliffe Road. My father walked across to the main road to catch a tram. I walked along the cinder path at the top side of the Wreck, then down Ram Lane to Ellen Brig and up the Scar. I did not see my father again that evening.

George Binns and my sister have gone. My mother is in bed.

To-morrow, old Flowerface and the children. It is strange, after almost twelve years, how much desire four days' absence can generate. I ought to be in Gwaelod by about eight o' clock in the evening. My mother will be joining us on Wednesday. She hasn't shown it, but the past eight days must have been a tremendous strain upon her. A week at the seaside will do her good.

If she was here with me now in the kitchen, I might, I suppose, be tempted to ask her questions about those few days twenty-one years ago. I might have been led on to tell her what I had seen at Gertie's back window. She might have raised again the question I asked myself then, whether it really would have been too late for me to do something if I had not so quickly been driven away by what I took for so improbable a bit of mere face-pulling.

For I said nothing, either about calling round at Gertie's that afternoon or about seeing Uncle Gordon come out of Law Barraclough's two days before his wedding. I said nothing later, when the homosexual scandal about Law Barraclough and Hinderholme United broke, though by then I was informed enough about such matters to see how the various episodes might be connected. Even before that, I'd read Freud and saw neatly enough that a man so desperate after a honeymoon must have failed badly at what a honeymoon is supposed to be for. I'd even gathered from some medical student one or two picturesque details of legal pathology and presented myself with the joke that, on coming home from her shopping that afternoon, Gertie might well have found Gordon's *membrum virile* in a potentially more satisfactory condition than heretofore.

I did not ask any questions. The family's verdict had been formulated. It was not fair to Gertie, who, after three days in a home of her own, had had to go back and live with her father and A'ntie Beulah. Uncle Gordon Broadbent's behaviour was judged inconsiderate.

At breakfast, the morning after the visit to Mr Beaumont's, my parents looked grave and secretive. As I came into the kitchen, my father was saying how hard it was on Gertie. Then nothing was said for a while. As my father got ready to go out, he and my mother looked at each other.

'You tell him, Ethel,' said my father.

My mother stood with the tea-pot in her hands and said:

'Harold, your Uncle Gordon's hanged himself.

Gertie came in from her shopping and found him there, still in his mill clothes. He hanged himself with his braces from a meat-hook in the kitchen. Gertie's very upset. She's gone back to live with Uncle Nathan and A'ntie Beulah.'

They looked at each other as if that was a load off both their minds. My father went off to work, chewing his moustache. My mother made a new pot of tea and addressed herself to the omelette machine.

CODA

A'NTIE ADA DIED NEXT DAY, THE MONDAY. MY
mother stayed for the funeral and did not join us at
Gwaelod till Thursday. Erica Jo and I went in to
Aberystwyth by Captain Lloyd's car. I remember my
mother bobbing gamely towards us along the platform,
followed by a porter. I remember the dazzling white of
her blouse, the smart costume. It was sunny.

I left them all at Gwaelod and went to lecture in
Oxford to a large extra-mural audience of foreign
students. My subject was the publisher's point of view.

Arthur Quarmby lasted until the winter. In February
this year, Blod and the children and I moved to Lower
Green Road, where we had more room, the sole advantage we have so far discovered in the neighbourhood, apart from the proximity of Tom Trufitt, a
Matthew Latimer author. We've had rather a lot of
medical troubles this year. My share of them was an
attack of jaundice.

Then Frankfurt, my old Rhineland haunts, Mme
Zix, a glimpse of Paris and Arlette. A bit more of Oxford. Four weeks of Scotland. I broke my return
journey at Leeds and rode into Hinderholme at the flat,

185

east-north-easterly end, past the British Dyes, the football ground and the gasworks, with Bradford Road below and a view of Cowl Hill beyond the town. I stayed one night at my mother's, and here I now am, travelling west-south-west towards Staleybridge. It is late November.

'That's the chair Dad collapsed in. He wet it through. It's got to be re-covered.'

There he would sit, take one boot off and ease the toes of that foot with his fingers. After a while, he would sigh deeply, take off the other boot, get his slippers out of the little cupboard at ground level, push his toes into the slippers and shuffle away. The chair has been re-covered in a rose-coloured plush. Formerly, it was dark green.

I saw no other change, except that my sister's piano has at last gone. Now I am to have the aspidistra stand and a carpet. A few things will go with my mother. The rest will be sold.

At first, my mother intended to keep the house on, though Marjorie and George Binns had already suggested that she go and live with them. There was talk of her taking in a lodger, but she does not fancy strangers in the house. Uncle Arthur, not managing very well on his own, wanted to lodge with her, but my mother, she said, could not have stood him about the place.

When Uncle Arthur died, he left my sister twenty pounds. It was, I fancy, all he had to leave. The furniture was somehow A'ntie Ada's and reverted to my mother. The twenty pounds went to my sister because, said Arthur, she had always been kind to him, the implication being that nobody else ever had. A'ntie Ada's wardrobe and dressing table are at Lower Green Road. They will go as soon as Blod has something better.

The piano went just before we moved from Pitt Rise. I had never grown accustomed to that dead reverberation, with its unquenchable echoes. It seems that new pianos are not being made. Since the war, there is no seasoned wood in the country. So dealers will buy anything which has an iron frame. I got twenty pounds in ready cash for A'ntie Ada's piano.

To get it installed at Pitt Rise, two enormous York-shiremen, a third who was smaller, a small but rosy German primitive painter and myself had struggled long. Two pasty young Cockneys, with long, dank hair, long, dusty, waisted overcoats, dirty pointed shoes, lifted it between them and were downstairs and out of the house in no time at all. I was glad to see it go. I had never needed it myself, as an instrument of retaliation against neighbours. Erica Jo had learnt her notes again, and A'ntie Ada could not be offended now.

I was for my mother keeping the house on. This was partly for selfish reasons. I felt that I ought still to have a headquarters in my native town, the more so as I was now head of the family. I thought I might go there more often. I even toyed with the notion of moving back to Hinderholme for good, making that my house, making my living by local journalism, regional broad-casting, giving up Matthew Latimer's, becoming the poet and thinker of a region. My roots were there, after all. Roots. Another dead metaphor. Men are not plants.

I did not toy long with that notion. Still, I should

have liked somewhere to stay, at need, in Hinderholme. Once my mother has followed the piano to Lancashire, I shall have no relations in the town, with the exception of a cousin of my father's who gave me my first piano lessons when I was five and whom I have not seen for years.

But I was also a bit concerned with my sister. George Binns is a slow-minded, easy-going, tolerant, good-natured fellow. I suppose he may even like my mother. Still, that is a very young marriage. A resident mother-in-law is a dangerous thing. I don't want Marjorie's life to come unstuck as a result of the two of them letting themselves in for a classical situation.

My mother is iron-willed and by nature intolerant. Also, despite her leg, she is physically tough. She will live fifteen or twenty years more. However, my sister's *démarche* lets me out.

'I've begun to feel that I'm one on my own,' is what my mother says.

One night, she thought she heard movement and voices at the back. In the morning, she found the front door of the passage unbolted. Somebody must have come from the allotments and through the garden. This upset her. In fact, she admits that this is what decided her to move. But, also, money can't have been easy. What my father left amounted, with the insurance, only to seven hundred pounds. The house ought to fetch fifteen hundred or even two thousand at to-day's prices.

And so I suppose I have finished with Hinderholme. It won't matter. That is not the centre of my life.

I felt nothing as, from the train, I looked down into Thwaite, where my father worked during the four years before we moved to Carlin Beck. As the train clung to high ground, canal and river both rose towards it, the square and hexagonal chimneys reaching up to carriage-window height. Those great square mills were admirable on a winter evening, their lights twice reflected in river and canal, but other people besides me have admired them. They belong to the memory.

To the left, I saw the entrance to the canal tunnel under the Pennines. Tearing into its own tunnel, the train screamed, but without urgency. It screamed again as it emerged, and the blackened stone walls of a cutting fell sharply away from the windows. That was no anthropomorphic cry, no example of the pathetic fallacy. A train whistle is a whistle, blown by steam.

Now the train bears left in a wide sweep through Staleybridge. The stone landscape gives out. This is already Cheshire. Soon I shall be riding due south through the brick Midlands.

If consciousness streams, it is backward. Or, rather, it is like the slack tide in an estuary. As I approach London, no doubt new urgencies will begin. At present, it is almost as though I were out on the open sea, glassily calm. If I again let down the deep trawl of memory, I should bring up dabs and elvers by the ton. The catch would only be to throw back.